FACING THE CHALLENGE

COMMON ISSUES IN WORK WITH PEOPLE WHO ARE MENTALLY
HANDICAPPED, ELDERLY OR CHRONICALLY MENTALLY ILL

Edited by

SARA SIMPSON
PETER HIGSON
ROD HOLLAND
JUDITH MCBRIEN
JOHN WILLIAMS
LYNDA HENNEMAN

BRITISH ASSOCIATION FOR BEHAVIOURAL PSYCHOTHERAPY

Ⓒ 1984 BABP Publications

29 OSBORNE WAY, HELMSHORE, ROSSENDALE, LANCASHIRE, BB4 4DX, U.K.

ISBN 0 9509539 0 3

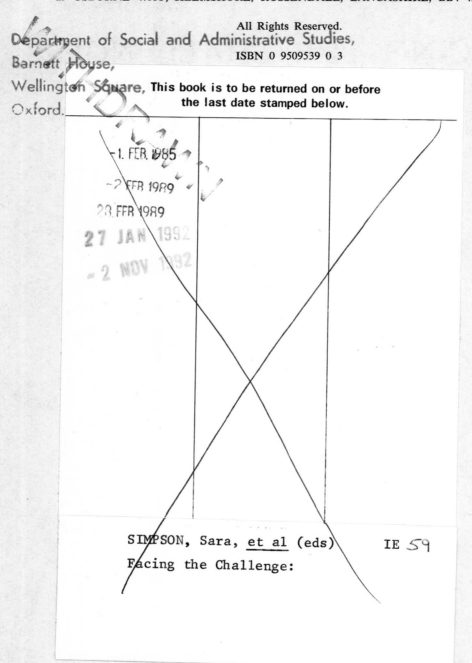

SIMPSON, Sara, _et al_ (eds)   IE 59
Facing the Challenge:

Printed and bound in Wales by
GEE & SON, (DENBIGH) LTD., DENBIGH, CLWYD.

Contents

Section Four: Interventions

A. People with Long-Term Psychiatric Disability

B. The Elderly

C. People with Mental Handicap

Section Five: Evaluation

Contributors

Christine Barrowclough, Senior Clinical Psychologist, Prestwich Hospital, Manchester.

Betty Bud, Superintendent Physiotherapist, St. Lawrence's Hospital, Caterham, Surrey.

Nan Carle, Research and Development Officer, Lewisham and North Southwark Health Authority, London.

Paul Chamberlain, Senior Clinical Psychologist, Coldeast Hospital, Southampton.

Baburao Chaparala, Consultant Psychiatrist, Dudley Road Hospital, Birmingham.

Sally Cheseldine, Senior Clinical Psychologist, Oldham Health Authority, Oldham.

Alison Cooper, Senior Community Psychologist, Social Services Department, Stratford, London.

Peter Davidson, Assistant Director, Solihull Social Services, Birmingham.

Guy Ekisa, Consultant Psychiatrist, St. Crispin Hospital, Northampton.

Sue Ferguson, Principal Clinical Psychologist, Psychology Services, Dorchester, Dorset.

Geoff Garland, Principal Clinical Psychologist, Warneford Hospital, Oxford.

Colin Grierson, Rehabilitation Officer, Birmingham Association for Mental Health, Charles Davis House, Birmingham.

John Hall, District Psychologist, Warneford Hospital, Oxford.

Adrian Hallmark, Occupational Psychologist, Manpower Services Commission, Manchester.

John Hattersley, Top Grade Clinical Psychologist, Brunswick House, Sheffield.

Lynda Henneman, Principal Clinical Psychologist, Exe Vale Hospital, Exminster, Devon.

Kevin Hewitt, Senior Clinical Psychologist, Stoke Park Hospital, Bristol.

Peter Higson, Senior Clinical Psychologist, North Wales Hospital, Denbigh.

Rod Holland, Principal Clinical Psychologist, Basingstoke District Hospital, Basingstoke.

Peter Horrocks, Director, Health Advisory Service, Sutton, Surrey.

Judy James, Principal Clinical Psychologist, Winsely Centre, Bath.

Nick Moffat, Senior Clinical Psychologist, East Dorset Health Authority, Poole, Dorset.

Reg Morris, Senior Lecturer in Clinical Psychology, Plymouth Polytechnic, Plymouth.

Margaret Mullen, Person in Charge, Mary Rose House, Havant, Hampshire.

Judith McBrien, Senior Lecturer/Senior Clinical Psychologist, Plymouth Polytechnic, Plymouth.

Neil McNeil, Senior Nurse, St. Mary's Hospital, Axminster.

Alison Norman, Director, Centre for Policy on Ageing, London.

Mark O'Callaghan, Senior Clinical Psychologist, Hollymoor Hospital, Birmingham.

Trevor O'Neill, Officer in Charge, Flint Green House, Birmingham.

Andrew Quarry, Principal Clinical Psychologist, Severalls Hospital, Colchester.

Kunal Raychaudhuri, Consultant Psychiatrist, Hollymoor Hospital, Birmingham.

Geoff Shepherd, Principal Clinical Psychologist, Fulbourne Hospital, Cambridge.

Sara Simpson, Senior Clinical Psychologist, St. Crispin Hospital, Northampton.

Caroline Sincock, Senior Clinical Psychologist, Prestwich Hospital, Manchester.

Nicholas Tarrier, Senior Clinical Psychologist, Prestwich Hospital, Manchester.

Charles Twining, Principal Clinical Psychologist, Cardiff Royal Infirmary, Cardiff.

Patrick Wallace, C.Q.S.W. Course, Selly Oak College, Birmingham.

Peter Wilcock, District Clinical Psychologist, Friar's Gate Medical Centre, Winchester.

John Williams, Principal Clinical Psychologist, Wingfield Mansions, Plymouth.

Bob Woods, Lecturer in Clinical Psychology, Bethlem Royal Hospital, London.

Peter Woods, Principal Clinical Psychologist, Bryn-y-Neuadd, Llanfairfechan, Gwynedd.

Preface

The papers presented in this publication developed from part of the proceedings of the 11th Annual Conference of the British Association for Behavioural Psychotherapy which took place at the Lawns Centre, University of Hull in July 1983. The BABP is a multi-disciplinary organisation open to all members of the helping professions and was founded in 1972. The objects of the Association are to promote the advancement of the theory and practice of behavioural psychotherapy, to provide a forum for discussion, to disseminate information, to promote research and to assist in training. The Association runs regular programmes of training workshops and conferences both at the national and regional level.

At the 11th Annual Conference the major emphasis was on work with people who are mentally handicapped, elderly or chronically mentally ill. These groups have traditionally been devalued by both society and the helping professions, but more recently there has been an increasing interest in work in these areas. In each field, however, developments have typically occurred in isolation, yet the issues faced by service planners, providers, consumers and researchers across the groups bear many similarities. For these reasons the BABP devoted a major part of its conference to the theme 'Facing the Challenge' which involved an examination of the concepts, advances and problems within each of these areas. More importantly, the three day event was planned in order to also provide a forum where the common issues could be examined in order that a productive interchange of ideas would occur.

The success of the Conference resulted in the suggestion by many of the participants that it would be a worthwhile venture for the Association to publish in as full a form as possible the proceedings. With much hard work by those who contributed to the conference and with the support of the Association we have succeeded in producing and publishing this record of the proceedings of 'Facing the Challenge', almost in its entirety, in a form which will allow the reader to follow and, we hope, find interesting.

ROD HOLLAND

Introduction

Facing the Challenge

ROD HOLLAND and SARA SIMPSON

Over the past few years there has been an increasing willingness by the helping professions to direct their attention and develop their skills towards those people that have tended to remain a low priority in any care service — the 'Cinderella' client groups. A degree of optimism has been generated by many people working in these areas who recognise that adopting a more positive philosophy of care results in significant improvement in the lives of people who are elderly, mentally handicapped or who have long-term psychiatric disabilities. The progress still to be made is greater than that already accomplished but it is possible to recognise some steps forward.

Behavioural approaches have contributed significantly towards offering more positive ways of helping both clients and professional workers. Conferences, workshops and journal articles of the British Association for Behavioural Psychotherapy and of similar organisations have reflected an awareness of the applicability of behavioural approaches with these groups. A large proportion of the multidisciplinary membership of the BABP is involved with handicapped people at a variety of levels, from direct care staff delivering services to those who have some responsibility for influencing their planning and organisation. The 1983 Annual Conference of the Association provided an opportunity to consider current work and developments in the field under the title 'Facing the Challenge'.

Although it would have been possible to put together a conference programme presenting material about highly refined intervention techniques, it was felt that there was a greater need to consider the broader issues that form the background for the implementation of these techniques. We know that specific programmes of behavioural intervention can be effective in helping these people, but there is an increasing recognition that the broader social and environmental setting in which the handicapped person lives is an important determinant of the success of any specific intervention,

1

as well as having a more general influence on the nature of that person's life. The knowledge that a particular behavioural training method is useful, for example, in developing independent care skills is not enough to lead to the adoption of that method in many of our current services. Instead, staff attempting to introduce and sustain new methods of working will be confronted by the problems familiar to all those working with handicapped people — problems such as trying to introduce innovative methods in traditional settings, keeping such methods going with clients who may only change very slowly, working in underfunded, inappropriately designed and sited facilities, trying to work with other disciplines and coordinate efforts with different agencies, and being aware that colleagues and society as a whole may view one's work as unimportant.

It is because general issues of this type and the problems at all levels arising from them are familiar to people working in each client group, that an attempt was made to plan and integrate a conference programme so that the common issues could be identified and a cross-fertilisation of ideas could occur.

Common Issues

It is possible to identify three fundamental issues that are common features of the lives of the three client groups: *social devaluation, disability* and *continuing or long term need.*

It is not the disability alone that creates problems for an individual but society's response that very often handicaps the person. The perception of handicapped people as fundamentally different from others in society, and the social devaluation which this perception frequently entails, has a profound influence on the nature of services that have been established in the past and are continuing to be developed. The paper by Nan Carle describes the process of social devaluation and considers how a different perspective can guide the development of a service which recognises the individual rights and needs of its consumers.

The nature and organisation of many of our traditional services results in interventions that are often dependency increasing. Whilst a person with a disability may have need for a service, the nature of the service provided should be one that *enables* the support of the individual despite the impairment. For example, as suggested by Peter Horrocks, a frail elderly person should be provided with adequate levels of support in the home rather than be offered residential placement. Other papers in section 3 consider ways in which service planning and delivery can be developed and John Hall's paper in section 5 examines how these services can be evaluated.

Many disabled people have difficulties which continue over long periods of time. However, the services they frequently encounter are often based on models of the acute treatment of disease and its cure, for example, hospital-based services. The difficulty clients have in responding to these often inappropriate models can lead to a sense of failure in the staff. Where more appropriate interventions are being used there is a further difficulty in sustaining them over long periods of time and ways need to be found for achieving this. Woods and Higson, and Chamberlain and Mullen, for example, consider possible solutions to this problem. Also, because of the long-term nature of the services they need to be organised in such a way that innovations can be introduced and change achieved and maintained. Section 2 considers this important area in some detail. Finally, many agencies may be involved over periods of time and effective coordination needs to be organised, as Alison Cooper emphasizes in her paper.

The common issues are reflected in different ways throughout the papers that follow. Despite the problems outlined, valuable work with these client groups is being done and its diversity is reflected in the papers in section 4.

The conference papers and the discussion that resulted confirmed that a consideration of the broader issues outlined above is essential to the success of further development with these groups. The issues are complex but it is obvious that people working with each client group can learn a lot from the experiences of those working in the other areas. The challenge of providing adequate and positive care for handicapped people will continue.

Common Issues in Work with People who are Mentally Handicapped, Elderly or Chronically Mentally Ill

Resolving 'Scull's Dilemma': Quality of Care in Hospital and in the Community

GEOFF SHEPHERD

The title of this paper is taken from an article in last year's British Journal of Psychiatry by Kathleen Jones (Jones, 1982). It refers to the work of an American professor of sociology, Andrew Scull, who has written extensively on the history and care of the mentally ill (Scull, 1977; 1979). He has been generally critical of what has been provided for the mentally ill both in hospital and outside it and Jones suggests that his main conclusion can be summarised in the following paradox: 'If it is wrong to get patients out of the mental hospital, and wrong to keep them in, what are we to do with them?' (p. 221, *op. cit.*). Since this seems to embody a widespread feeling 'Scull's dilemma' will be used here to analyse in what sense it may be wrong — or right — to look after patients in hospital or in the community and in what ways this apparent dilemma can be resolved. It will be argued that the 'dilemma' stems from a false polarisation between hospital and community. It also fails to consider *quality* of care offered by mental health services and this needs to be analysed in terms of staff-patient interaction, organisation and management practices, and the overall comprehensiveness of the service system that is provided.

Firstly, it is disappointing to note that some twenty years after the first concerted efforts were made to care for the long-term mentally ill outside hospital, people are still presenting care in hospital and care in the community as if they were opposing, even mutually exclusive, alternatives. Surely it is not a case of care in hospital *or* care in the community, but the relative balance betwen in-patient and community-based services? Clearly, there are some patients who can only be managed safely in hospital. Most studies of day treatment exclude certain categories of acute patients. Many acute psychiatric patients may thus require a short period of in-patient care initially, so that their symptoms can be effectively treated, they can then be returned

4

to the community to receive further treatment and care in day programmes, etc. What needs to be reviewed is therefore not the existence of acute in-patient treatment *per se*, but criteria for admission, lengths of admission, and the extent to which day programmes are available with appropriate medical, as well as social and psychological, supports. If these kinds of facilities are present, then the studies cited above suggest that a substantial number of acute admissions can be avoided, or at least reduced (Herz, 1982).

In addition to in-patient care for the acutely disturbed, there is also a need for provision for the long-term disturbed patient. The 'new' long-stay have been studied by Wykes (1982), Bachrach (1982), and others. Data from the Camberwell Register, and from our own research, suggests that the annual rate of accumulation of these patients may in fact be quite small. Thus, we are now accepting only approximately 10-15 new patients into long-stay beds each year from a population of approximately 500,000. This gives an annual incidence rate of only 2-3/100,000, which is very similar to the Camberwell figure (Wykes, 1982). It should also be noted that with intensive rehabilitation, not all of these new long-stay patients will necessarily then stay in hospital indefinitely.

In addition to new long-stay in-patients, there are also still large numbers of 'old' long-stay residents in our mental hospitals. According to the latest DHSS figures there are about 60,000 of these and their numbers are reducing slowly (DHSS, 1983). These patients are now increasingly elderly and frail, the majority being aged over 65, with multiple physical, psychiatric and social disabilities. They remain in hospital either out of choice, or because there are simply no alternatives available in the community. Unless there is suddenly an enormous expansion of sheltered accommodation (including Part III for the elderly) we must therefore expect that these older long-stay patients will continue to need hospital care for some time to come. For many, hospital has become their home and it is neither ethical, nor feasible, to attempt to move them now.

So, there are a number of reasons why we cannot think of a simple choice between hospital and community care. As Leona Bachrach pointed out some years ago, there should have been a move away from, 'the polarised anti-hospital stance that characterised the early years of the deinstitutionalization movement' (Bachrach, 1980; p. 1025). The debate should now be about how much in-patient care we require, where, and of what kind. The problem is to avoid under or over-provision of either kind of facility. Also, to ensure that the in-patient services co-ordinate effectively with day and other community-based care. On the basis of experience with the Worcester Development Project, the Department of Health now seem less convinced of the general usefulness of the acute unit in the district general hospital. So, perhaps there are possibilities now for planning 'upside-down' psychiatric services (Bennett, 1978) where day places predominate over beds, instead of the other way around.

Of course, resolving the problems of providing a good quality of care in hospital and in the community is not simply about getting the right balance between the different kinds of service. Quality of care depends upon *what* is provided, not simply *where* it is provided. Basing services in the community is certainly no guarantee that good quality services will necessarily result (Shepherd and Richardson, 1979;

Shepherd, 1981). We therefore need to examine in detail what we mean by 'quality of care' and how we might evaluate whether or not it is actually occurring.

'Quality of care' is a composite of several variables. Each one is a necessary, but not sufficient, condition and their interaction is important. Can we start to identify these variables? Let us consider three different levels: (1) staff-patient interaction, (2) organisation and management practices, and (3) the overall comprehensiveness of the service 'system' provided. Specifying effective care at the level of staff-patient interaction is relatively straightforward. We can assume that a minimum amount of staff-patient interaction must occur, and thus first we must counter the natural tendency for staff in institutional settings to withdraw from patients and spend more time interacting with one another than with their clients. Token economies and other ward-based management programmes seem effective ways of achieving this, and the research suggests that social reinforcement (praise, encouragement, etc.), is the most important ingredient in maintaining behavioural change (Hall, Baker and Hutchinson, 1977). The actual physical administration of tokens only seems important for the most severely disabled patients (Paul and Lentz, 1977) and during the acquisition phase (Elliot, Barlow, Hooper and Kingerlee, 1979). In addition to these quantitative aspects of staff-client interaction, there are also rather more subtle qualitative aspects. It is harder to point to the literature in support of this, but is seems likely that the 'therapist variables' which are so widely accepted as being important throughout the field of adult psychotherapy are also important in counteracting the depersonalising tendencies of institutional environments.

Of course, effective staff-patient interaction is not enough by itself. All interactions take place within an overall organisational context and the characteristics of this context, its policies and procedures can effectively support or inhibit particular patterns of staff-client interaction from occurring. There has now been considerable research to identify the key dimensions of management practice which are associated with 'client-oriented' or 'institutionally-oriented' patterns of care (Raynes, Pratt and Roses, 1979) and of these, individually-centred management programmes seem the most important (Bachrach, 1980). We must also examine the physical setting, its characteristics and potential for eliciting and maintaining adaptive behaviour (Whatmore, Durward and Kushlick, 1975) and other possible constraints, for example: overall size of the unit; staffing ratios and stability and deployment of staff at peak times; staff involvement in decision-making (Raynes, Pratt and Roses, 1979) attitudes and morale (Watts and Bennett, 1983). Indentification of these variables and an understanding of their interaction, in particular their effects on staff and clients' behaviour, seem crucial areas for future research (Shepherd, 1983).

Finally, we come to the question of the overall quality of service 'system' provided. Leona Bachrach (1978) has also analysed the implications for service systems of attempting to cut down on hospital-based care. She argues that unless we understand very clearly the functions (social, residential, occupational, etc.) which mental hospitals served, we will not be able to replace them with effective alternatives in the community. More recently, the DHSS has attempted to set out the minimum elements of a comprehensive, district-based, mental health service (DHSS, 1983). In essence both these approaches argue for a range of services (in-patient, out-patient, day patient) with different levels of service (residential and day-care) geared to different levels of client need. We have also recently attempted to sketch out the elements of a comprehensive day service to meet our local needs. There is therefore clearly a move away from a unitary model of community care towards one based on a recognition of the specific service needs of specific client groups.

All this implies considerable feats of communication between the different agencies involved and considerable investment of capital and revenues to create these new services. Perhaps it is fitting then to conclude with a quote from a more recent paper by Andrew Scull where he comments on the current enthusiasm for 'deinstitutionalisation' in the US and the UK. He notes that 'the shift away from the mental hospital in both societies has been powerfully influenced by fiscal considerations, the savings realisable by substituting neglect for even minimal custodial care' (Scull, 1983; p. 345). This seems a much more profound dilemma. If we are to successfully resist the movement to neglect the chronic patient, we must at least understand what it is we should be fighting for. Perhaps then Scull's other dilemma may not be so defeating after all.

References:

BACHRACH, L. L. (1978) A conceptual approach to deinstitutionalisation. *Hospital and Community Psychiatry, 29,* 573-578.

BACHRACH, L. L. (1980) Overview: Model programmes for chronic mental patients. *American Journal of Psychiatry, 137,* 1023-1031.

BACHRACH, L. L. (1982) Young adult chronic patients: An analytical review of the literature. *Hospital and Community Psychiatry, 33,* 189-197.

BENNETT, D. H. (1978) *The Role of the Day Hospital. In Report of a Seminar on Day Care for the Mentally Ill.* London: D.H.S.S.

Department of Health and Social Security (1983) *Mental Illness: Policies for Prevention, Treatment, Rehabilitation and Care.* London: D.H.S.S.

ELLIOT, P. A., BARLOW, F., HOOPER, A. and KINGERLEE, P. E. (1979) Maintaining patients improvements in a token economy. *Behaviour Research and Therapy, 17,* 355-367.

HALL, J. N., BAKER, R. D., and HUTCHINSON, K. (1977) A controlled evaluation of token economy procedures with chronic schizophrenic patients. *Behaviour Research and Therapy, 15,* 261-283.

HERZ, M. I. (1982) Research overview in day treatment. *International Journal of Partial Hospitalization, 1,* 33-44.

JONES, K. (1982) Scull's Dilemma. *British Journal of Psychiatry, 141,* 221-226.

PAUL, G. L., and LENTZ, R. J. (1977) *Psychosocial Treatment of Chronic Mental Patients: Milieu versus Social-Learning Programs.* Cambridge, Mass.: Harvard University Press.

RAYNES, N., PRATT, M., and ROSES, S. (1979) *Organisational Structure and the Care of the Mentally Handicapped.* London: Croom Helm.

SCULL, A. (1977) *Decarceration: Community Treatment and the Deviant: A Radical View.* New York: Prentice Hall.

SCULL, A. (1979) *Museums of Madness: The Social Organisation of Insanity in 19th Century England.* London: Allen Lane.

SCULL, A. (1983) The asylum as community or the community as asylum: paradoxes and contradictions of mental health care. In P. Bean (Ed.), *Mental Illness: Changes and Trends.* Chichester: Wiley.

SHEPHERD, G. (1981) Day care and the chronic patient. In *New Directions for Psychiatric Day Services.* London: MIND.

SHEPHERD, G. (1983) *Institutional Care and Rehabilitation.* London: Longmans, (In Press).

SHEPHERD, G., and RICHARDSON, A. (1979) Organisation and interaction in psychiatric day centres. *Psychological Medicine, 9,* 573-579.

WATTS, F. N. and BENNETT, D. H. (1983) Management of the staff team. In F. N. Watts and D. H. Bennett (Eds.), *Theory and Practice in Psychiatric Rehabilitation.* London: Wiley.

WHATMORE, R., DURWARD, L. and KUSHLICK, A. (1975) Measuring the quality of residential care. *Behaviour Research and Therapy, 13,* 227-236.

WYKES, T. (1982) A hostel-ward for 'new' long-stay patients: An evaluative study of 'a ward in a house'. In J. K. Wing (Ed), *Long-Term Community Care: Experience in a London Borough. Psychological Medicine,* Monograph Supplement 2. Cambridge: Cambridge University Press.

Common Experiences of People with Handicapping Conditions – Normalisation and Implications for Service Development

NAN CARLE

There has been much discussion about 'Care in the Community' as a new approach to delivering services to people with handicapping conditions. However, from my point of view, it is important to understand that the concept of community care is a vague and incoherent one full of competing conceptions and contradictions.

During the last seven years I have been involved in promoting ideas such as 'Normalisation' and 'Core and Cluster', seven years on, however, I visit places and I hear about the 'Normalisation Room'. Or, I hear about the new 'Core and Cluster Scheme' in which the local hospital where 125 people live is the 'Core' or the local hostel where 20 people live is the 'Core'.

The 'Core and Cluster' model of residential services was certainly developed as a way to address the organisation of residential services. However the services themselves were for very small numbers of people living in ordinary housing, as do the rest of the people in a given community. In addition, since 1975 the 'Core and Cluster' model has dropped the 'Core' as a place where handicapped people live and has evolved to be purely an administrative core, i.e. the office.

Unfortunately many service providers have picked up the language and merely attached it to inappropriate practices of the past, without regard to the fundamental principles on which the ideas are based.

Therefore the debate between 'hospital' provision and 'community' provision must be a careful one in which terms are explicitly defined. We do not have to go very far to see services currently available in the community which are very segregated, very isolated and very institutional. We are in danger of recreating the practices which in the past have caused public scandal — just in smaller settings. It is ways in which we can move away from that danger which I intend to address in this paper.

Common Experiences

A starting point is an examination of the way in which the general public thinks about people who experience handicapping conditions. They may consider people with handicaps to be sick and in need of a cure, or as childlike and in need of protection. Recently there has been a growing perception of handicapped people as a commodity to shift about *en masse* as expenditure items. Certainly the general public does not hold the people in our services in high esteem. These attitudes about differentness are similar regardless of whether a person experiences mental handicap, mental illness or old age.

People in these services are considered different and this difference is not considered a positive one. The general reaction is one of creating distance. Unfortunately whether one is a nurse, social worker, doctor or an administrator, one is influenced by these prevailing attitudes.

The experience of handicapped people of this 'distance' can be described in the following examples:

Separate and Unequal: The language we use often indicates ways in which we keep people apart from ourselves and from other non-handicapped people. This has become more subtle as we learn more about language and behaviour. In the field of mental handicap we are trying to get away from using the term 'mongol', when we talk about people who experience Down's syndrome. However, in the press and even in the professional literature the term 'Down's syndrome' is bracketed by the word mongol.

The location of our service is another indicator of creating distance and separateness. Services are being located on existing health or social service property. For people with handicapping conditions it means yet another ghetto where large numbers of people with a similar label are placed, or other people with 'special needs' are located. One housing estate in London has a disproportionately high number of families with handicapped members, or with members known to social services. It is social services policy to locate such individuals and their families in a certain part of the borough and on a particular housing estate. In other places, especially around the coast of England, the large houses and hotels that fewer and fewer single families can afford to run, become private or public residential facilities.

The final and perhaps most profound way services keep people with and people without handicaps apart is through the practice of grouping large numbers of people together. It is the one way to make absolutely certain that the negative stereotypes are perpetuated. The probability that positive experiences occur between people who are and who are not handicapped is nil.

If I am sick what's the cure? People who find themselves in our services are usually given a type of therapy. Thus we have work therapy, music therapy, sex therapy, horticultural therapy and recently I heard someone lecture on bibliotherapy. All that the rest of us consider fun or do by choice has become a therapy for those people receiving a service. Much of the reason for so much 'therapy' is because of the funding structure. Money is more likely to be made available for therapy than for having a good time, or for everyday responsibilities and opportunities. Unfortunately funding structures are not value free. They do influence the type of services that are provided and the way consumers and others respond to it. When the expected 'cure' is not forthcoming it may cause service providers and others to give up and to feel that the situation is hopeless. The type of service we get is one of containment.

It is my observation that in the UK, there is not an aggressive use of teaching technology to teach people to be far more independent and to do far more complex skills than they do at present. Our expectations of people with handicaps is typically low — no cure — no hope. The experience of people in our services is often one of never being quite good enough.

Cold as Charity: For people with handicaps this is not a trite expression. One of the most valued aspects of our western culture is to be able to return a favour, to reciprocate a gift. When people accept a service this dignity is often not allowed to them. The unspoken rule is 'be thankful for what you have, and do not ask for anything more'.

For adults spending time in day centres the system of benefits and pay creates severe disincentives to want to work and to be able to work. The packaging done by people in various day centres is work done only in such service facilities. Managers have unhappy stories about companies playing one centre off against another for the lowest price. This makes it impossible to receive a fair price for work done. The experience of the person with the handicap is a 'charitable' £1 to £4 per week for their labour.

The Boy who Never Grew: For people in our services be they labelled psychiatric, mentally handicapped or elderly, the prevailing practice of treating adults as children, either because they are in their 'second childhood' or are forever children, creates obstacles to enabling people to take risks and to be seen as capable of achieving new skills. Frequently there is a great deal of protection. It is not just the fault of the parents. In one day centre for physically handicapped people they are actively discouraged from leaving the building, even though the surrounding neighbourhood and riverside has been made accessible for those using wheelchairs. Day centres often exist to occupy peoples' time, i.e. they provide a minding service for parents or families.

To be sure, many people truly enjoy attending these facilities. However, the question must be asked 'what *real* choices does each person have?' and further 'how could the unique skills of each person be developed into competencies wanted and needed by society at large?'

One of the fundamental principles in developing and maintaining our own personal interests is to be able to redress what happens to us. This is even more important for those people who do not, or cannot speak for themselves. Unfortunately it is not yet commonplace in our services for people to be involved in decisions about where they may live, who they may live with or even what they will have for dinner. The experience for people in our service is all too often that of powerlessness.

The Future

Obviously not everyone in our services is subject to all the experiences I have mentioned and some of our efforts to change what is happening are very positive. However, the 'experiences' or themes do exist and are likely to continue unless we begin to face and meet specific challenges about what we are doing and how we are doing it. One response which I have found particularly helpful in providing parameters for positive problem solving is the principle of normalisation as put forth by Wolf Wolfensberger. His work has been further elaborated by John O'Brien and adapted for British readership by Alan Tyne. The definition of normalisation is as follows:

> *The use of means which are valued in our society in order to develop and support personal behaviour, skills, experiences, and characteristics which are likewise valued.*

This definition has two components. The first is concerned with what a service does: the goals that are set, the settings chosen, the staff employed, the language used, and the way peoples' time is structured.

The second component is what a service accomplishes: the images created, the personal continuity experienced by those using the service, the competencies learned by individuals, relationships maintained and developed, and the real options available to each person.

The principle of normalisation suggests that we strive for that which is the most desirable and consistent with the highest expectations of the general public. If error is made it should be toward the most valued option, especially as a way to over-compensate for all the negative expectations and practices that people have been exposed to. The word normalisation is a word which Wolfensberger recently suggested was a bad choice. It traps people into debates about what is normal. Wolfensberger now writes about 'social valorization'.

In this context normal means: (a) A range of familiar and valued options — not a single right answer. (b) A judgement in terms of the experiences and aspirations of typical and valued people in a given culture — not in terms of what is common for people with handicaps.

The work of Thomas Gilbert and John O'Brien suggests the following areas towards which we can strive to make accomplishments: community presence, promotion of individual interests and protection of individual rights, continuous growth and development, positive reputation, and community participation.

These accomplishments are inter-related to discussions about who a person is in terms of their strengths and abilities; the goals selected to work on; the process used to meet stated goals; and who should be involved.

Guidelines for Service Design and Delivery

The following guidelines may be useful in thinking about designing and delivering services, regardless of the persons' handicapping condition.

* Focus on what the strengths and needs are of each individual.
* Disperse and integrate rather than congregate and segregate.
* Use the most valued option.
* Place service (or activity) in culturally typical settings — at 'natural' times.

11

* Help eliminate rather than magnify negative images.
* Focus on practices and accomplishments not intentions .
* Involve consumers in decisions being made which affect them.
* These ideas are not just for some but for everyone.

Conclusion

I have tried to make the point that our community services are in danger of merely re-creating inappropriate and institutional practices. Any debate about 'care in the community' must have very well defined parameters. Community presence is only a pre-condition for being more accepted and part of the community at large. The principle of normalisation offers a response which can push back at institutional practices. It helps set ideal standards that can help us maintain continuity in direction and cohesiveness in our actions. It also helps us in times of compromise to know what we can sacrifice in a manner that is consistent with what we are trying to do. It is essential that we now join forces with peoples' natural networks, such as their families, friends, neighbours, and so forth to provide a place for everyone to live in the community.

The greatest good for the greatest number must be sought in future terms. A great many generations may suffer from our well intentioned but short-sighted services.

References:

FLYNN, R. J. and NITSCH, K. E. (1980) (Eds.) *Normalisation, Social Integration and Community Services*. Maryland, Baltimore: University Park Press.

GILBERT, T. (1977) *Human Competence: Engineering Working Performance*. London: McGraw Hill.

O'BRIEN, J., and TYNE, A. (1981) *The Principle of Normalisation: A Foundation for Effective Services*. London: CMH.

WOLFENSBERGER, W. and GLENN, L. (1975) *Program Aanalysis of Service Systems*. Third Edition. Toronto: National Institute of Mental Retardation.

WOLFENSBERGER, W. and THOMAS, S. (1983) *Program Analysis of Service Systems. Implementation of Normalisation Goals*. Toronto: National Institute of Mental Retardation.

Discussion

Discussion after the first session of the Conference reflected the common concerns of those working with people with long-term psychiatric or mental handicaps, or with those who are elderly. The main issues considered were, how to develop an alternative community-based pattern of services, what are the ingredients of such a service that are necessary in order to meet clients' needs, and how can the effectiveness of such services be measured?

Reflecting the emphasis of Nan Carle's paper, the importance of ideology not only in determining the nature of services but also as a means of actually achieving change was stressed. The need to educate the public if communities are going to accept a different pattern of care for their handicapped members was noted and ways in which this can be done discussed. The point was made that public education is taking place every day as a result of the buildings and services provided for handicapped people and as a result of what we do with them in public. However, the message conveyed is generally a negative one that perpetuates images of differentness and devaluation. It was suggested that those in the caring professions should look outside their own areas of expertise and make use of the knowledge of other fields such as the advertising industry in order to change public attitudes. Individual contact between handicapped and non-handicapped people was seen as one of the most effective ways of encouraging more positive attitudes. Finally, the usefulness of consumer groups in campaigning for different types of services was commented upon.

Concerning the necessary ingredients of community-based services, there was much discussion about the inadequacy of vague concepts such as 'community care'. Instead there is a need to be precise about the objectives of a service and to specify in detail its operating practices; for example, the use of individual programme planning systems or of particular types and levels of staff-client interaction.

It was a common experience that once-off programmes introduced by personnel external to day or residential facilities produced only short-term effects, and the necessity for a management infrastructure to support any innovations was emphasised. Some expressed hope that because of the individual-centred nature of the Nursing Process it may help support direct care staff in activities different from those characteristic of long-stay facilities.

One point was raised concerning a difference between service delivery to people with long-term handicaps and those with short-term difficulties. Since the former are likely to remain within the service for long periods, successive goal setting for each individual is required if the service is not to be merely custodial, whereas people with short-term problems are likely to terminate their contact with the service once a set of goals is achieved. Services for people with long-term handicaps, then, need to incorporate methods that ensure that clients' progress is regularly reviewed and new goals for each individual are set.

Finally, practical difficulties for staff working in community-based services were commented upon, in particular the special problems that may arise from the geographical dispersal of facilities.

Across all three client groups there was interest in criteria for evaluating community based services. There was considerable concern that the present government is encouraging the development of community care because it views it as a cheaper option, and there was emphasis on the need to specify the cost-*effectiveness*, involving the measurement of the output of a service, or its 'quality of care', as well as the resources put in. There is a need for the complex of variables encompassed in a concept like 'quality of care' to be precisely defined, and for the use of traditional administrative indices of effectiveness such as bed occupancy or hospital admission rates to be discouraged. Whilst some professions may have well-developed evaluation skills it was considered important that evaluation should be an in-built feature of a service's operation, and all staff involved in the service should see this evaluation as part of their role.

Achieving and Maintaining Change

'Systems Run Best Downhill': Facilitating Change in Organizations

LYNDA HENNEMAN

Anyone who has tried to help organizations change knows the frustration of seeing systems revert to old practices as soon as you leave — or even before you go. Genuine change is recognizable because it is self-maintaining and therefore persists.

An inspection of the management charts and operational policies describing lines of accountability and decision-making procedures may seduce you into believing that care-delivery systems are rational creatures whose only aim is to provide the best possible service for their clients. My experience does not bear this out. I now realize that trying to change an organization is very like the clinical task of helping a person change. For example:

1. The 'presenting problem' can be of only marginal relevance. It is often a 'ticket in' to finding help for a much more complex and ill-defined situation.
2. Any intervention can have unexpected outcomes because you may unknowingly destabilize a larger system.
3. They can 'get better' for ecological reasons which have little to do with your intervention.
4. Organizations, like people you have helped, can become dependent. Occasionally to the extent of finding new problems to keep you interested.
5. Unless you like wasting your time, you should only proceed with their consent.

This similarity is more than a metaphor — in both situations the task is to help a SYSTEM change.

To change a system, it is essential to understand something of its nature. Success is unlikely if you proceed on the basis of what *should be* the case. Just as 'the chart is not the patient', so the management chart or operational policy is not the organization.

The form of systems' behaviour is very similar although its content will vary with the level of system; whether it's an individual, a family or an organization.

14

1. *A 'hierarchy of needs'* operates, (Maslow, 1954). This means that first needs must be satisfied before a system will give time and energy to fulfilling needs higher up the hierarchy. At the bottom of the hierarchy are SURVIVAL AND SECURITY. In any organization, these needs have priority over any external goals. In other words: INTRA-SYSTEM GOALS COME FIRST. Within an organization, even on the simplest analysis, there are several sub-systems to consider (Herbert, 1981):

formal system	informal 'social' system	Total 'individuals'	}	Organization

So any intervention which threatens the survival or security of any of these systems diverts energy to ensuring that these needs are still satisfied. The effects of the recent NHS reorganization are an excellent example that many of us are familiar with.

2. *Systems seek equilibrium and a particular fit with their environment.* They operate efficiently when system resources and external demands are roughly in balance. Nahemow and Lawton's (1973) diagram illustrating ecological adaptation summarizes this point.

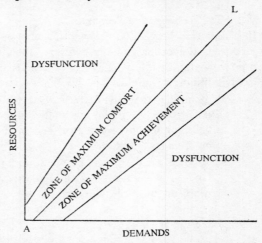

Equilibrium is maintained by responding to feedback. If resources drop, then the range of situations which can be coped with must constrict if balance is to be retained.

In human systems, of course, equilibrium is a balance of *perceived* resources and demands. So it can remain stable by for example, not perceiving additional demands.

The sort of change produced by adaptation is rarely planned. It evolves organically in response to changing circumstances. So the sum of such adaptive changes can be apparently inappropriate or irrational behaviour. Disturbing these behaviours should not, however, be undertaken lightly, at least until you have some idea of why they came about.

We can now see why change is so often resisted. Any change potentially threatens the safety and security of a system and destabilizes its 'fit' with its environment. For change to be possible:

perceived cost of change < perceived cost of no change

Facilitating change therefore involves reducing the perceived cost of change and/or increasing the cost of no-change.

3. *Systems behaviour is extremely complex*
The behaviour of a system is a function of:
    (a) The nature of the elements.
    (b) Their organization/relationship with each other.
    (c) The relationship of a system with its ecosystem.

15

The corollaries of this are:
- (a) Causation is often complex to the point of incomprehensibility.
- (b) Unpredicted side-effects should be expected.
- (c) Intervening in one system will frequently disturb an adjacent system which was previously working well.

Changing Systems

Facilitating change is clearly a delicate task. In general 'systems run best downhill' (Gall, 1979), that is to say they work best when designed to take account of human motivation, and any change strategist should keep this in mind. In this paper I shall limit myself to three operating principles to guide planning for change. (Ackoff, 1974).

1. *The Participative Principle*

It is usually believed that the main benefits of planning come from acting on the plans produced. We believe, to the contrary, that 'the principal benefit of planning comes from engaging in it. In planning, process is the most important product'. This belief has two important implications for the way change is planned:
- (a) It implies that it is better to plan for oneself, no matter how badly, than to be planned for by others, no matter how well. This commitment to participation calls for the involvement of everyone who can be affected by the plans made, or their representatives.
- (b) Change agents should be facilitators of the planning of others for themselves. One of the advantages of a participative approach is that there are fewer problems in implementation.

2. *Principle of Continuity*

As we have stressed, it is almost never possible to understand completely the casual links in a system. Even the best-laid plans can produce unanticipated effects. 'In the normal course of events, planning stops when implementation begins. Such planning is discontinuous; it should be continuous'. Plans should be constantly revised in the light of (i) their performance, (ii) unexpected problems and opportunities that arise, and (iii) the latest information and knowledge available. Much of this is learned from the process of implementation.

3. *Holistic Principle*

Because problems do not exist in isolation, but are elements in a system of problems, 'every part of a system and every level of it should be planned for simultaneously and interdependently'. As opposed to the two common practices of top-down and bottom-up planning.

This means adopting a goal-directed, constructional approach rather than being problem-orientated.

In summary, sustained change is more reliably achieved by a process of guided evolution than by 'hero-innovator' catalysed revolution.

References:

ACKOFF, R. L. (1974) The systems revolution. *Long Range Planning, 7,* 2-5.
GALL, J. (1979) *Systemantics.* London: Fontana.
HERBERT, T. T. (1981) *Dimensions of Organisational Behaviour.* London, Macmillan.
MASLOW, A. H. (1954) *Motivation and Personality.* New York: Harper.
NAHEMOWL, L. and LAWTON, M. P. (1973) Ecology and Adaptation in the Ageing Process. In C. Eisdorfer and M. P. Lawton, (Eds.), *Psychology of the Ageing Process.* American Psychological Association.

A Working Model for Creating Change

SUSAN FERGUSON

Unfortunately for those of us wishing to achieve change, organisations naturally seek equilibrium and in order to do this, they resist change.

Kurt Lewin's Force-Field theory shows us that the greater the pressure for change, the greater the resistance. But change is necessary for growth and adaptation to changing needs, particularly in service delivery.

A systems approach shows us that the participative approach is necessary for successful, lasting and adaptive change. After all, the implementers of the service are the instruments through which change is achieved and a participative approach commits them to change in which they have been involved at a planning stage.

This is the Action Research paradigm (Ketterer, Price and Polister, 1980), now a well-developed research paradigm for social and health research, as it has been for many years in industry. The model has been summarised by Kurt Lewin and we have adapted his theory into our model for change:

1. Unfreeze: consists of loosening up the system in a planned way, to make it susceptible to change.
2. Change: involves moving, that is creating actual changes in attitude or behaviour.
3. Re-freeze: means stabilizing the change at a new level of functioning.

Foster prescribes certain guidelines for achieving this, drawn from Lewin's writings. Firstly, identify the influentials or gatekeepers; secondly, study the social context in which gatekeeper behaviour takes place; thirdly, utilize problem-posing in groups to increase participation; and lastly, use experts to feed information to groups as required.

We have adapted and refined this into a working change model for ourselves: the 'Ferguson/Henneman' model.

UNFREEZE — CHANGE — RE-FREEZE

UNFREEZE involves loosening up the existing system in a planned way — a preparation stage which can take a year or two. Several tactics are possible:

1. Look for signs that it is a suitable time for change. These may take the form of new demands on the organisation (reorganisation, enquiries, government reports, requests for surveys, or figures, demands for new practices such as normalisation, or demands for improvements such as Hospital Advisory Service reports); new resources being made available (end of financial year, capital savings, joint financing, voluntary monies, gifts of equipment or volunteers), rumours of change or times of changing morale either up or down; staff changes including arrival of new staff (before they get sucked into the old system) or departure of old staff (who may have been blocking change). Alternatively the organisation, or part of it, may have asked for your help. Beware! They may not really want what they have asked for, or understand that their practices may have to change too. However, if you can find out what is behind their request, it may be a situation that you can use.

2. Identify key people. Gatekeepers are people whose permission or approval you need. They may be officer in charge, ward sister, or merely a care assistant who organises the daily routine of residents. They are potential blockers and they have motives of their own, both professional and personal, with loyalties, long memories for past failures of innovation, and an informal social structure which will be of paramount importance to them. Allies, others who want change, may be found at all levels, and some of these may become catalysts to action especially if you can find them in key places such as a nursing officer, a budget-holder, or a member of a management or planning team. At all times we need to be aware of those with power particularly personal or social standing, hierarchical power, access to resources and those with knowledge and skills.

3. Scout potential obstacles. There are thousands of possibilities but some will particularly apply to your setting and may affect implementation of change. They can be organisational, such as record-keeping methods, systems for ordering equipment, the time-table, too few occupational therapists, lack of monitoring of staff activities, absence of operational policies; or they may be social, such as the way the grapevine works, sister's affair with the consultant, staff's relationship by marriage to one of the gatekeepers, or who drinks with who in the social club.

4. Look for a soft spot, a point of entry. In most networks, alterations at some places are likely to have more profound effects on the system than alterations at others, like moving a card from the top or bottom of a house of cards. We also need to find the soft spot where entry will be easiest. It is not a fixed characteristic, depending on the state of the network and will not be the same on each ward, on each occasion, or in each organisation. So a tactic you have used successfully in the past may not be useful in a new situation. If no soft spot can be found because at each point you encounter a double-bind, excuses or procrastinations, all is not lost. You may try altering as many links in the net-

work as possible simultaneously and observe the ripple effect. Even if you are only able to alter your input to the system, this will have a knock-on effect, producing other minor changes until soft spots become apparent. Failing that, look at the wider context and use the next level up (go to the management team) or try a flange attack on an adjacent system (offer your services to the ward next door and wait for your initial target to get jealous).

5. Determine your mandate to proceed. Are they ready for change? Are you? Why now? Do you have an invitation/permission to proceed? Do you want to? Would it be better left alone? Is it a can of worms you would rather have nothing to do with?

CHANGE occurs when deliberate action takes place and unfreezing will already have started this. But look for both the expected (potential obstacles) and unexpected effects of unfreezing. On the grounds that any activity produces change, and if taking a baseline can change behaviour, so will a questionnaire, survey, workshop or pilot project.

Here change may occur without people realising it — the foot in the door technique. Since the participative approach is most likely to succeed, involving people in monitoring or evaluation tasks produces ideas, identifies gaps and enables staff to identify their own operational problems and goals by which they would like to be evaluated in the future. Poverty of ideas can be dealt with by generating ideas through brain-storming, visiting other units, or by you putting up plans which they can criticise or demolish. Carrots work better than sticks and goal-setting exercises lead easily both down to day-to-day sub-goals and activities, and up to operational policies. In order to ensure their implementation it is necessary to discover or set up the organisational structure that will be necessary to support the plans, and maintenance strategies can be devised which ensure — refreezing.

RE-FREEZE means shaking down into a new system which must be more flexible than the old or future change will not be possible. It involves:

1. Maintenance Strategies. These must include feedback (efficient record-keeping, regular assessment, keeping up a flow of information, asking people, clients, relatives what they think of the service); monitoring (report regularly to someone even if they don't ask it, meet regularly, preferably by keeping on the original planning group, evaluate); increase the status of the new system by inviting visitors or managers to view the excellence of your service, even before it is excellent; write it up and help others to write about it in their own journals, tell them how well they are doing, continue training and increasing their skills, invite criticism and build up some Dunkirk spirit among the staff; maintain enthusiasm yourself and don't back out too soon.

2. Leave them with tasks to do and problems still to be tackled.

3. Leave the possibility for future change by leaving it with as little system as possible — few rules, don't print the assessment and record charts, etc.

4. Build in how you or other key people may leave it without it collapsing.

A new system can only survive in its new form for a limited time before it must change again in response to new demands, so be prepared and make yourself available to go back later and help them change again.

References:

KETTERER, R. F., PRICE, R. H. and POLISTER, P. E. (1980) The action research paradigm. In R. H. Price (Ed.). Evaluation and Action in a Social Environment. London: Academic Press.

Creating and Maintaining Behavioural Change in an Institutional Setting – The Ivanhoe Project

PETER WILCOCK

This paper describes events between 1973-1977 in a large 650-bedded hospital for mentally handicapped people.

I was a recently qualified psychologist and this was my first job. I thought I'd be welcomed! I was appointed to cover the 'children's unit' which comprised four modern single storey villas. I was determined that my role would be intervention rather than assessment. I moved my office on to one of the wards to be more accessible, and after three months was totally demoralised. It seemed that I was more likely to achieve something If I concentrated on one villa only.

This was a villa for 24 profoundly handicapped and behaviourally disturbed children. It was perceived as the punishment villa for both staff and children and its geographical position underlined this — isolated from the rest of the hospital, hidden behind a small hill and, literally, at the end of the road. There was a considerable conflict between staff on the villa, and all-in-all it was considered an embarrassment to the hospital. Visitors were steered round it. But it was felt that some behaviour modification programmes would probably improve things.

Another significant influence was the fact that the hospital wanted to run the J.B.C.N.S. Behaviour Modification Course but were hampered because no behaviour modification was being carried out. So a working party was established to look at ways of introducing the methods. I was a member of this working party which recommended that the villa should be the starting point. It recommended, further, that new specialist staff should be appointed to establish a staff training team; videotape and two-way screen equipment should be purchased; the Regional Board be asked for financing. This was November, 1973.

Early Developments

The basic working party recommendations were accepted in principle within the hospital *but* no extra money was allocated for revenue expenditure. A joint psychologist/SNO paper was produced which in retrospect did more harm than good. A new ward sister was transferred onto the ward to support the development *but* the care staff were unchanged. The number of children was reduced from 24 to 16. This was on-stage. Off-stage, there were considerable personality difficulties within the nursing hierarchy that complicated matters. One off-shoot of this was the setting up of a competitive scheme on another villa. The nursing officer supported the villa, but only as a way of getting at the senior nursing officer.

November 1974 — The First Mistake

The Policy Team was formed 'to consider requests from the ward sister and charge nurse to implement such changes in ward management as might be agreed' and 'to have responsibility to co-ordinate and ensure the smooth running of the villa so that programmes could be implemented'. Its members were ward charge nurse and sister, unit nursing officer, nursing officer (training) and clinical psychologist.

The Children's Management Team was also formed. This included all the villa staff and its aim was to consider the needs of individual children and draw up training programmes.

Following its first meeting the Policy Team made its first and last mistake. The minutes referred to the difficulties experienced by the NO in maintaining staff levels because of new and competing demands from a project on one of the other villas. This team only met once again before a memo from the SNO burst upon the scene and brought things to a standstill. He pointed out that despite high staffing levels no 'programme' existed and therefore recommended a reduction in staff available to the ward. He neglected to mention that the nature of the children on the villa required more staff simply to provide custodial care; although numbers were high the staff were changed frequently and many were of very poor quality; the new sister was on extended sick-leave.

December 1974 - November 1975 — Picking up the Pieces

The H.M.T. set up a small sub-group to consider the scheme's difficulties. They reported in January 1975 and recommended that the project should continue. They also agreed to look at the staffing problems.

There were middle and senior management changes during this period. These resulted in a more sympathetic NO arriving on the scene and the return of the PNO who was totally committed to the development. By September 1975, agreement had been reached about staff. New staff would be appointed specifically for the villa and in future there would be no staff-rotation for any reason. These decisions were significant in that they provided the opportunity for us to move forward. Therefore we had a clearer idea of where we wanted to go. We were quite clear that we wanted to create a 'home' rather than simply a Behaviour Modification Unit because: (1) there was no point intensively teaching skills to children who had no opportunity to use them and (2) it was useless to use intensive behavioural programmes to eliminate behaviours that were the product of a deviant environment. We now had the opportunity to look at the entire working of the villa rather than just the children and their behaviour. Specifically (1) to develop real team management within the Villa, (2) to develop as engaging an environment as possible, (3) to consider the individual needs of the children and set longitudinal objectives. We began to consider a number of issues such as staff attitudes, training, motivation and allocation, the co-operation of other hospital departments, decision-making procedures, relative roles of different grades of staff.

December 1795 - December 1976 — The New Beginning

New staff were appointed and trained. Although staff training had been carried out for some considerable time it had previously been unsuccessful because (1) they were not interested or committed, (2) training was squeezed into times when children were off the ward, and (3) they had little opportunity to use their training in their day-to-day work.

The new villa policy team was formed. This time *all* staff on the villa, day and night, were members, and attendance was almost mandatory.

Its function was to agree changes in ward policy and management and to co-ordinate the running of the villa and the implementation of teaching programmes. At its first meeting children and staff were divided into three groups. Each group held a weekly group meeting where their children were discussed individually and day-to-day teaching decisions taken.

Thus, the structure was very emphatically a team structure operating at two levels. It worked very well because (1) all staff had a say in decisions affecting their work, (2) it did not depend on one personality to keep it going, and (3) it helped staff to see themselves as part of a team, (this was also helped by hostility from the rest of the hospital).

However, after about twelve months some unforseen difficulties arose. Nursing assistants would on occasion refuse to carry out a request from qualified staff until it had been agreed by the policy team. On the other hand, qualified staff felt threatened (1) by this, (2) by always having to explain themselves, (3) by the absence of a forum where they could discuss their own management problems, and (4) the unclear guidelines about where the limits of their authority lay.

Winter 1976/77 — Re-Tuning

It was decided to review the management structure and the policy team set up a working party consisting of qualified staff, nursing assistants, the NO and the psychologist. It agreed to the establishment of a *non-executive* 'senior staff' meeting as recognition that the qualified staff did have statutory duties. However, the policy-forming body would remain the policy team.

I am sure that this was one of the fundamental reasons for the continuing evolution of the villa as a place where children's needs were paramount, decisions were implemented, and some dramatic changes occurred. Anybody attacking or disrupting the villa had to be prepared to take on the entire staff! Two other points: (1) because decisions were agreed publicly and recorded, the staff identified for action were more

22

likely to implement the decision, (2) the fact that nursing assistants were being monitored by their peers was probably more effective than the traditional hierarchial supervision.

In Retrospect — Making Sense of It All

When we started we had no idea of where we were and only an ill-formed idea of where we wanted to go.

We used the desire for a J.B.C.N.S. course as the opportunity to push for more fundamental change. This was opportune for me after my early experience of failure.

I now see that the rollercoaster of the next two years was merely the system unfreezing!

When we did succeed in creating change our planning was participative and involved many different parts of the system. Moreover, we remained open to new information and were able to change our plans appropriately.

The Re-freezing process contained many of the elements described in Sue Ferguson's paper:

1. The new system was flexible — it made and changed its own rules.

2. Although there was no formal evaluation, regular feedback was built into the system. The assessment of the children for a research project showed considerable gains in a wide range of areas.

3. The status of the ward increased. The villa changed from one that was never visited to a hospital showpiece, (despite the fact that it was never written up!!).

4. Enthusiasm was also maintained by frequent contact with the psychologist and PNO visits to the villa.

5. Although we didn't invite criticism, we got it from the rest of the hospital who resented this concentration on a single villa. Our nurses were dubbed 'super-nurses'.

6. We tried to build in self-sufficiency and avoided developing a cult-figure. Eventually the role of the psychologist was re-negotiated through the policy team and my time there was reduced.

Service Planning and Development

A. PEOPLE WITH LONG-TERM PSYCHIATRIC DISABILITY

Comprehensive Service Provision for the Long-Term Mentally Ill.

GUY EKISA

The long-term mentally ill comprise a heterogeneous group with varying degrees of disability. Generally, many tend to be poorly motivated, chronically relapsing, psycho-socially disadvantaged individuals who show poor community survival skills. Left unsupported, in a harsh world, they tend to be re-admitted, aimlessly wander the streets, are solitary or end up in penal institutions. In other words, they form the high risk population group.

The annual re-admission rates for this population group are between 50% and 70% (Anthony, Cohen and Vitato 1972). Traditional aftercare practices (injection clinics, day hospitals, visits, and occupation in workshops, etc.) have been unsuccessful in maintaining these patients' 'survival skills' or reducing the revolving door problem.

Alternatives to In-Patient Treatment.

Research findings have demonstrated that alternatives to hospital in-patient treatment (day care centres, half-way houses, hostels, specific family interventions) can be effective in maintaining patients in the community (Test and Stein, 1978; Mosher and Menn, 1978; Rosenfield, 1982; Paul and Lentz, 1977).

Edmonson, Kinder and Marlowe (1979) have advocated a community network development system of care with special emphasis on a peer support system of mangement. They assert that while most mental health services tend to focus on improving patients' internal resources (psychological, biological, etc.) the peer support system of management concentrates on the patients' external resources. Thus social network and supportive systems are seen as essential to an individual's community adjustment. Unlike 'normal' people, chronic psychiatric patients tend to have fewer social network

24

members, and in times of crisis these individuals tend either not to mobilise their networks appropriately or to rely heavily on professional care givers. In a preliminary report Edmonson et al., randomly allocated 80 subjects to two groups during their last weeks of hospital treatment. Upon discharge, control subjects were referred to the traditional aftercare services while the experimental subjects were referred to the community network development programme. Ten months later all the subjects were interviewed. The results showed that the experimental subjects were better adjusted than the controls in terms of requiring less psychiatric treatment, spending fewer days hospitalised, and having fewer hours of out-patient contact.

Although these studies suffer from various methodological problems, tentative conclusions appear to be that:

1. These innovative programmes reduce admission rates but do not prevent them. They are no worse than in-patient care, and positive results are associated with high staff-to-patient ratios and guaranteed funding.

2. They serve as substitutes for traditional in-patient care. They are effective, particularly if the programmes are individualised.

3. There is no evidence of a reduction of symptom levels.

4. Improved psychosocial functioning is only seen in very intensive programmes targeted specifically towards psychosocial areas. This benefit lasts only as long as treatment continues, i.e. there is poor generalisation.

5. Patients report 'satisfaction' with them.

The importance of aftercare support is amply highlighted by Mosher and Keith (1979). They concluded 'given a behaviourally-oriented programme with aftercare and adequate community residential facilities and programmes, more than 90% of very chronic patients can be discharged into the community with a two year readmission rate of less than 5%. Although only 10% of these are able to function completely independently, the rest are able to function well enough to fulfil their basic needs for food, shelter, socialisation and recreation.' The emphasis here is on the value of aftercare support. What is clear, therefore, is that neither the institution alone nor the community alone can handle the problems of long-term patients. The two need to be integrated and seen as complementing each other.

Characteristics of the community supportive system.

The Community supportive system is defined as the network of caring and responsible people committed to assisting a vulnerable population to meet their needs and develop their potential without being unnecessarily isolated or excluded from the community (Turner and Shifren, 1979). Community supportive system criteria include:

1. A mechanism for identifying this client group and a means of reaching out to them.

2. Assistance in applying for and obtaining benefits.

3. 24-hour crisis support.

4. The provision of psychosocial rehabilitation.

5. Services of indefinite duration.
6. Adequate medical and mental health care.
7. Back-up support for families and significant others.
8. The engagement and involvement of the community.
9. The protection of rights and civil liberties.
10. Integrated and co-ordinated services.

Such a community supportive system is necessary as a response to the progressive nuclearization of the family, and is intended to provide the support that has been lost because of the dissolution of the extended kinship network or residence in hospital, (Mosher and Keith, 1979).

Although chronic patients are no different from anyone else in needing social support networks to maintain themselves, they unfortunately have such serious and persistent emotional disabilities that they are unable to develop and maintain such networks without special help (Test and Stein, 1978).

An Integrated Community Mental Health Service

The development of an effective District Psychiatric Service calls for a shift from the traditional Mental Illness Service focus to the Community Mental Health Service focus, with more emphasis on developing a comprehensive infra-structure of graded living accommodation and innovative community day care systems, including the recruitment of non professionals. This comprehensive infra-structure should complement the psychiatric in-patient resources and the traditional family supportive networks. The facilities created should be available to all the clinical teams on a sector-ised basis.

While there are obvious functional overlaps between Day Hospitals and Day Centres, Day Hospitals may be seen as primary treatment facilities offering acute and active treatments or training, while Day Centres are secondary treatment facilities offering maintenance and supportive care. Thus the bulk of long-term community clients could essentially be supported in Day Centres and only referred to Day Hospitals for specific treatment/training as appropriate.

Such a comprehensive mental health service therefore would comprise hierarchical treatment involving day supportive and residential resources commensurate with the clients' functional level and degree of support/care required.

An example of an infra-structure of community resources would include:

1. *Day Care Systems.*

   (i) Day Hospitals — primary facility.
   (ii) Day Centres (Social Services, MIND, etc.) — secondary facility.
   (iii) Recreational and socialisation facilities (selected community centres, etc.).
   (iv) Vocational Facilities —

   > Training
   > Sheltered
   > Specific Projects

2. *Graded Residential Resources.*

    (i) Own houses/flats.

    (ii) Group homes.

    (iii) Long stay hostels.

    (iv) Supported homes/flats.

    (v) Supervised lodgings (approved).

    (vi) Long stay ward (behaviourally disturbed).

The key to the establishment of a Community Mental Health Service is the availability of graded day care and residential resources in the community. Without this, there is usually an over-dependence on in-patient facilities, or a resigned acceptance of treatment in the home environment which are known to be pathotrophic.

References:

ANTHONY, W. A., COHEN, M. R. and VITALO, R. (1978) The measurement of rehabilitation outcome. *Schizophrenia Bulletin, 4,* 365-383.

BACHRACH, L. L. (1982) Assessment of outcomes in community support systems: Results, problems and limitations. *Schizophrenia Bulletin, 8,* 39-60.

EDMONSON, KINDER and MARLOWE (1979) Personal communication.

FALLOON, I. R. H. and MARSHAL, G. N. (1983) Residential care and social behaviour: A study of rehabilitation needs. *Psychological Medicine, 13,* 341-347.

MOSHER, L. R. and KEITH, S. J. (1979) Research in the psychosocial treatment of schizophrenia. *American Journal of Psychiatry, 136,* 623-631.

MOSHER, L. R. and MENN, A. Z. (1978) Community residential treatment for schizophrenia: Two year follow up. *Hospital and Community Psychiatry, 29,* 715-723.

PAUL, G. L. and LENTZ, R. J. (1977) *Psychosocial Treatment of Chronic Mental Patients: Milieu versus Social-Learning Programmes.* Cambridge, Mass.: Harvard University Press.

ROSENFELD, A. H. (1982) Closing the revolving door through family therapy. *Hospital and Community Psychiatry, 33,* 893-894.

TEST, M. A. and STEIN, L. I. (1978) Community treatment of the chronic patient: Research overview. *Schizophrenia Bulletin, 4,* 350-364.

TURNER, J. E. C. and SHIFREN, I. (1979) Community support systems: How comprehensive? *New Directions for Mental Health Services, 2,* 1-12.

Developing Current Services – St. John's Hospital, Aylesbury

ANDREW QUARRY

This paper is an account of the way in which long-stay rehabilitation services at St. John's Hospital have evolved over the last eight years. The intention is not however to describe the operation of a major innovative scheme. Much of the current work being done borrows selectively from concepts and models which have been researched or piloted elsewhere, and which would commonly be found in any recent overview of the topic (e.g. Wing and Morris, 1981). The aim, instead, is to outline the way in which some of these ideas have been implemented in a setting which is not especially unique or privileged but which is probably fairly representative of many traditional psychiatric hospitals.

St. John's Hospital is a Victorian-designed building which is sited approximately three miles from the nearest centre of population, Aylesbury. It has a total population of 420 patients. 240 of these comprise the long-stay, ostensibly non-psychogeriatric, sector although (40%) are over the age of 65. The mean age of the long-stay residents is 60 years and the mean length of stay is 20 years. There are 10 long-stay wards in all, and one mixed, 44-bedded Rehabilitation Unit, Beacon House whose function it is to prepare selected individuals for resettlement. Although younger and less chronic than those in the other wards, most of these residents would be considered to fall into the 'old' long-stay category (Mann and Cree, 1976) of patients who have lived in hospital for over three years at least.

Rehabilitation services are planned and co-ordinated by a multi-disciplinary team, the Rehabilitation Sub-Committee. Although nominally responsible to the Division of Psychiatry, it has an important executive function in terms of organization of services, for instance, the management and apportionment of recently allocated money from Joint Funding.

The 11 members span all the professions involved in rehabilitation. Despite its size this committee has managed to smooth the path for change. Its effectiveness derives partly from the fact that it includes all those who have a particular interest in and responsibility for rehabilitation within their separate disciplines. This helps to ensure a strong commitment to the decisions which are made and maximizes the likelihood of their being carried out. Another factor is that two-thirds of the Hospital Management Team are also Sub-Committee members. This arrangement provides informed representation of rehabilitation interests in terms of overall hospital policy.

When planning major changes within the long-stay area, the Sub-Committee tends to be guided by an implicit 'problem-solving' strategy. The main stages are:

1. *Collect information* about problem, e.g. by means of a survey.

2. *Set priorities* based on this information.

3. *Examine options,* i.e. available ways of achieving priority goals.

4. *Implement 'best' option.*

5. *Evaluate consequences.*

This process is streamlined by the creation of small working parties which report back to the Committee upon the completion of designated tasks. For instance, most of the information gathering and the generation of options is accomplished by the working party while decisions about priorities and the selection of the 'best' option are the result of consensus within the full committee.

The above approach probably evolved rather than appeared as a deliberate attempt at rational planning. Likewise, the contribution of the Sub-Committee has only gradually become more incisive with time and experience, playing only a minor role in the first recent phase of organized rehabilitation at St. John's. This occurred over the period 1975-81 and involved the establishment of group homes for patients who were relatively able, and who did not require extensive training over and above a 3-6 month preparation in a hospital-based flat. This was carried out by enthusiastic individual staff and was initially very successful. However, there was a marked lack of inter-disciplinary involvement at clinical and administrative levels and, latterly, relapse rates became unacceptably high as the number of suitable residents diminished.

The second, overlapping, phase began in 1979. One long-stay ward was beginning to experiment with a more systematic approach to the development of community 'survival' skills, based on social learning or behavioural principles. A small pilot project provided the impetus for the establishment of a specialized unit via the rejuvenated Rehabilitation Sub-Committee. A survey helped to identify potential candidates and also focused attention on other aspects of long-term care, e.g. heterogeneous mix of patients in many wards. The training period prior to resettlement had to be extended up to 18 months. Greater consideration was given to type of placements and to the provision of adequate after-care resources.

A third phase is now beginning as the second gathers momentum. It involves looking more closely at the residual hospital population and, simultaneously, at the development of day-care and other support facilities outside hospital. Better ways of organizing the remaining long-stay residents into functional groups are being examined. As before, a survey has assisted in the identification of priorities and, to some extent, in the evaluation of the second phase.

Effective rehabilitation is a complex business which, like any successful enterprise, may owe as much to the conjunction of the right people in the right place at the right time and to fortuitous events, as to the operation of systematic planning procedures. These considerations aside, however, the necessary conditions would appear, at the very least, to include the effective involvement of all disciplines in the planning and implementation of services, consensus decision-making and the capacity to critically appraise the consequences of such decisions.

References:

MANN, S. and CREE, W. (1976) 'New' long-stay psychiatric patients: A national survey of fifteen mental hospitals in England and Wales 1972/73. *Psychological Medicine, 6,* 603-616.

WING, J. K. and MORRIS, B. (1981) *Handbook of Psychiatric Rehabilitation Practice.* Oxford: Oxford University Press.

Towards the Development of a Comprehensive Rehabilitation and Continuing Community Psychiatric Support System

MARK O'CALLAGHAN   PATRICK WALLACE

PETER DAVIDSON   COLIN GRIERSON

KUNAL RAYCHAUDHURI   BABURAO CHAPARALA

Hollymoor Hospital Rehabilitation Unit and Middlewood House Social Services Rehabilitation Centre form the latest designated National Demonstration Centre for Rehabilitation. The road to this status was not an easy one and illustrates many of the difficulties facing service planners and providers in the field of psychiatric rehabilitation in particular, and in many other areas as well.

Our first task, that of changing an already existing rehabilitation system, illustrates a particular difficulty facing such systems; that of rigidity and therefore inability to adapt to new demands or external circumstances. This is more likely to happen if the unit has been successful.

The rehabilitation unit was established in 1972 and achieved great success through the use of a Token Economy system and other means in discharging long-stay patients back to the community such that the hospital now has less than half the 800 inpatients it had in the 1950's. However, it continued to function in the same way until the reorganisation in late 1979/early 1980 in that it still had its focus of training on the long-stay even though a different type of patient was needing different types of programmes. With the addition of a day centre and the reorganisation of residential facilities, the rehabilitation unit was better able to cope with this new population consisting of the 'new chronics' and 'revolving door' patients, as well as the traditional longer-stay population.

So much for changing an already existing system. The task of developing a rehabilitation system in Solihull Social Services which was complementary to that of the hospital was made easier by a joint appointment (presently joint financed) of a clinical psychologist to both rehabilitation systems who could act as 'referee', having the interests of *both* places at heart as well as in helping develop joint policy documents, planning proposals, assessment forms and training processes for staff and rehabilitees. The new policy document drawn up for the hospital rehabilitation unit was essentially the same as that produced for Middlewood House.

Apart from both systems being complementary in terms of levels of independence, it was decided that the focus of each would be slightly different to provide a continuum of provision along the psychiatric-social dimension. A study of hospital admissions

30

carried out in the 1950's was repeated and it was found that although the inpatient numbers had dropped by about half, total admissions (both new and re-admissions, the latter accounting for about half total admissions) had also gone up by about the same amount. Many of these admissions had a large social component to them and so it was felt that by chanelling these towards Middlewood House, more appropriate help could be given to these people. However, whilst Middlewood House is not seen as a medical centre, it still needs the support of the hospital especially in those cases where, although there are social problems, there are also psychiatric difficulties as well.

In order to develop jointly we make use of two means for change. Firstly, we look for any external factors which might be useful. Thus, for example, some homes might become vacant and so we see if we could use this facility to both our benefits. Helping set up Birmingham Association of Mental Health's new rehabilitation hostel and another one run by Birmingham Social Services and COPEC Housing Association helps us both gain in the long run. Apart from having one person working at both units, the officer in charge (or deputy) at Middlewood House sits on the hospital rehabilitation planning sub-committee. Similarly, a charge nurse attends Middlewood's meetings. Every three months representatives from both committees attend a regular meeting on rehabilitation of the Care Planning Team for the mentally ill. Thus, planning can continue to be joint and involve those who actually work in the system. Another method by which we develop is by a six-monthly report conducted by the joint appointee based on routine statistics from the referral and assessment forms as well as from information given by members working at both establishments. Apart from preventing complacency, this report also serves to give staff some feedback as to how the system is progressing in that it looks not just at the successes but also at the gaps in the service. Clearly it would be useful to have a panel of experts in rehabilitation critically but friendly disposed to us that they could offer a constructive report on our work every so often. In the absence of this we rely on other outsiders to monitor parts of our work which then go into the main report.

So what are the gaps in the system or the difficulties that we face? Firstly, we have identified two groups of people whom we are not able to help adequately and for whom we may have to plan accordingly; these are the head injured and those who have both psychiatric and mental handicap difficulties. A proposal has already been made for a regional unit for the former. Secondly, we are not helping those people who have family/marital difficulties enough; one of our main causes for re-admission. We have tended to concentrate on the individual in isolation. Three new developments, namely an education package for relatives run by the National Schizophrenia Fellowship and a psychologist from Coventry, a relative support group and a family therapy project, should help here. Our other major reason for re-admission has been due to medication difficulties. Self medication programmes adopted throughout the system may reduce such re-admissions. Self neglect after discharge has remained a worry but with the increased move towards self catering in the rehabilitation unit this has been reduced except for those for whom self neglect is an aspect of severe loneliness, a major problem facing our clients when they go into the community and for whom, with

31

great difficulty, we are trying to provide a supportive social network. We face the problem of massive staff changes, especially when key members leave within a short space of time. It has been a process of having a monitoring function for those who remain in post together with interested parties that has kept us moving forward as well as the emphasis on using the different skills of new members to the advantage of the system. The strong emphasis on the close co-operation within and between units ensures that no one individual upsets the work being carried out. Finally, we face the problem of having close co-operation between the rehabilitation unit in the hospital and Middlewood House but difficulties with other units within the hospital. We are now trying to encourage closer working relationships here as well.

So we come finally to new developments. Mention has already been made of the opening of the new rehabilitation hostels. The rehabilitation unit at Hollymoor Hospital has been reorganised and a hospital hostel is planned. The family unit, set up by Middlewood House, has moved into new premises and will be independent but still linked to us. New social clubs are being set up for clients of both establishments. Planning for longer term supervised accommodation is our next priority and depends on finances being available. Perhaps with the Registration of Homes Act and the aid of the newly formed Solihull MIND we might be able to get this venture off the ground. Finally, although we are supposed to be providing a model of good rehabilitative practice for others as a National Demonstration Centre, we are very much aware of the need for our own staff for further training if we are not to end up with a static system, therefore training is being organised with the Birmingham University Extra-Mural Department and relevant agencies as much as finance and study leave time allow. The road to being a National Demonstration Centre in sum, then, was long but we still feel that we have a long way to go before we really provide a comprehensive rehabilitation and continuing community psychiatric support system.

Discussion

The presentations in this session had been selected in order to present an overview of the sorts of services needed by people with long-term psychiatric disabilities and to illustrate factors involved in service development by describing the ways in which two very different places are responding to the needs of their local populations. The discussion following these presentations was broad-ranging, but it is possible to summarise the main points raised under the following headings: the client population; the co-ordination of services; details of service provision; achieving change.

The Client Population

Those involved in the broad field of psychiatric rehabilitation are working with a range of different client groups. Traditionally, rehabilitation services were primarily concerned with the 'old long-stay' of psychiatric hospitals and many people, particularly those working in the larger hospitals, are still dealing mainly with this group. In other places services have been developed to help people who have had much shorter periods of residence in hospital (they may be referred to as the 'new long-stay' although there is no commonly agreed definition of this group). In yet other areas the population of concern may have high levels of contact with a broad range of services, such as hostels, day care and social work support, but spend relatively little time in hospital residential care. There is therefore a problem of definition and a need to clearly identify the differing specific difficulties and service needs of these people. The term 'rehabilitation' is perhaps becoming an inappropriate way to describe the very varying work going on with these client groups.

The Co-ordination of Services

The question arose of who should provide the service to these different client groups. There is clearly a need for considerable liaison between the health service, the local authority and the voluntary sector at both a planning and an operational level if services are going to be able to comprehensively meet clients' needs. Suggested ways of achieving better co-ordination were joint-funded projects and joint working arrangements such as joint meetings to plan individuals' goals where their achievement might involve different agencies.

A useful starting point for the development of services was thought to be a survey of what is currently available in a locality, particularly facilities provided by non-statutory agencies. It was thought that for some aspects of provision, for example, resources to meet people's long-term social and recreational needs, the statutory authorities should not aim to provide special facilities but should aim to integrate handicapped people into normal community facilities.

Since a large number of people receiving an acute model of psychiatric service in fact have long-term mental health and social difficulties, the problem of the interface between specialist rehabilitation services and the acute sector was raised. The view was expressed that rehabilitation services are often too isolated and are offered too late; instead, bridges need to be built between the two parts of the service. A suggested way of doing this was to establish a liaison group involving representatives of both parts of the service in order to develop joint projects. It was further suggested that whilst rehabilitation teams may need to spearhead the development of community based services for people with long-term disabilities; once established, elements of the service should be available to all clinical teams within a locality.

Details of Service Provision

Two principles considered concerned the need to offer levels of support to clients according to their level of functioning, and the need to provide the service in the place where people have difficulties. The former means that a broad range of facilities needs to be provided. In particular, problems of rehabilitating the old long-stay were

33

mentioned, the view being expressed that since in many places the more handicapped of this group are now entering rehabilitation programmes, there is a need to develop community accommodation offering higher levels of support than that traditionally available; for example, staff going in at critical periods of the day.

Regarding the second point, the recurrent problem of generalisation of training was debated. Wherever possible skills need to be taught in the situation where the skill is going to be performed. This requires a greater flexibility of service delivery than that common in most settings; for example, direct care staff need to be able to leave day and residential facilities and work with people in their own homes.

The advantages and disadvantages of grouping together people with varying levels of disability were discussed. Benefits were thought by some to be that the more handicapped people would benefit from being in a more active therapeutic environment and that staff morale would be higher. The alternative view was put forward that it is difficult to develop within one unit interventions to meet a wide range of needs. Clearly, if the objective of a service is to deliver interventions to meet individual needs the achievement of this objective will not depend on the functional grouping of clients alone, but on additional factors such as staffing levels and the skills of the staff and the management of the unit.

Finally, the need to take into account consumers' views of services and for practitioners to initiate research to answer the questions being raised in everyday practice was emphasised.

Achieving Change

The frustrations of attempting to influence systems were a common experience. The need to be involved at a planning level was stressed. One way of doing this if one has no formal authority is to present to planning teams information collected by the rehabilitation service, which is necessary to the planning process. Data evaluating the work of the local service were viewed as important, as was making available information about services and findings elsewhere. Involving external advisory bodies was also thought to be a useful way of facilitating change.

Finally, the opportunity to find out about the difficulties encountered by other services as well as their successes was considered a very useful way of gaining information necessary for the improvement of systems.

B. THE ELDERLY

The Integration of Services for the Elderly: The Current Situation

PETER HORROCKS

Present services for old people are grossly fragmented. This is the result of piecemeal legislation; low expectations for elderly people; the combination of unrestrained professionalism and professional neglect. There is no central agency which controls or co-ordinates service provision.

I should like to concentrate on just three commonly unresolved practical problems.

1. *Housing Needs of Elderly People*

   Where old people live is a key factor in how they cope with increasing fraility. We would agree (Shegog, 1981) that (a) except in extreme cases, help should be delivered in an old person's own home, (b) type, positioning and grouping of accommodation is crucial, (c) one move (but not several) is a reasonable strategy to offer a frail older person.

   Despite its importance, allocation of housing is done by local housing authorities without any consultation at all. Medical input if any is unspecialized. There is no attempt to identify the *cause* of the need for rehousing. Social Services may not be consulted. The request for a move for family reasons has very low priority. Special housing is built without allowances for disability. Wardens feel unsupported and are expected to provide services for which they are untrained. Housing authorities select only the fittest candidates, and deny places to those who would benefit most.

2. *Discharge from Hospital.*

   The return home from hospital is a time of high risk for elderly patients (Skeet, 1971). They are making the transition from a secure supportive environment where decision making has been minimised, to a situation where immediate self-determination must be maximal and less help is on hand. They are simultaneously crossing a deep inter-professional chasm. The resulting tragedies have been described:

   Community social services and nursing services may be ignorant of the discharge or slow to respond.

   Relatives may not be advised.

   The patient may forget advice.

   Hospital assumptions about home conditions may be completely unjustified.

3. *Services for the Elderly Mentally Ill*

The prevalence of mental illness of all sorts is high in old age (NCCOP, 1979). Much is due to or associated with physical illness. Its presentation is commonly in social terms (inability to cope, stress on relatives, risk to self or others).

The most predictable problem put to visiting HAS teams is the burden posed by the elderly mentally ill. Their nuisance value is described — blocking acute, orthopaedic, geriatric and mental illness services. GPs report patients bouncing from one agency to another, each denying responsibility on the basis of some arbitrary professional ruling. (The label 'psychogeriatric' might have been created to indicate responsibility lies elsewhere!)

Reference is made to the burdens born by families. Rarely, if ever, are the sufferer's experiences expressed as the justification for new approaches.

Solutions

These problems and most others faced by elderly people have in common the need for proper assessment for correct solution.

Assessment will always need to be multidisciplinary. No single discipline and no professional or voluntary agency acting alone will succeed. Assessment should consciously seek the client's view of the problem and available solutions, and his choice should be paramount.

Delivery of integrated services needs interdisciplinary co-operation of the highest degree (HAS, 1982). It requires broad consultation about proposed actions. It also implies participation, not just in case conferences, but in working parties, planning teams and committees of all sorts.

An Example

Techniques for ensuring the successful return home of elderly hospital patients

Early multidisciplinary planning of discharge.

Work interchange between hospital and community nursing staff.

Trial (assessment) home visits before discharge.

Hospital based domiciliary care officer with team of home helps to bridge gap until community based services begin.

Arrangement with LASS department for rapid provision of aids and adaptations.

A form issued by the hospital to the patient with details of medication, permitted activity, services arranged and follow up (e.g. day hospital).

Arrangements with ambulance service to ensure return home at a suitable time.

Attached community nurses who attend case conferences at which discharges are planned; visit the discharged patient within the week; 'fine-tune' arrangements which need adjusting; and report back to the hospital team on the success or otherwise of the discharge.

These are some of the techniques adopted by one hospital department of medicine for the elderly. As a result of these techniques, hospital staff have become aware of the need for careful planning. Information fedback by community nurses about discharged patients helps to strengthen and maintain the system.

There is a need to generalise such techniques into all hospital departments which care for older patients. The appointment of Aftercare Co-ordinators by Health Authorities has been proposed (Royal College of Physicians, 1981). All such arrangements are highly demanding on staff time and depend on motivation being created and sustained.

There is every reason to be optimistic about the elderly. They pose problems massively where their real needs are unrecognised and therefore unmet. They are often represented as posing an economic threat of infinite proportions to the health and social services. Effective services are not cheap but given adherence to the principles outlined, neither are their cost overwhelming. The example above demonstrates that solutions are not necessarily dependent on new resources for a new start to be made.

References:

Royal College of Physicians of London: Committee on Geriatrics (1981) Organic mental impairment in the elderly. *Journal of the Royal College of Physicians of London, 15,* 141-167.
Health Advisory Service (1982) *The Rising Tide: Developing Services for Mental Illness in Old Age.* London: DHSS.
Continuing Care Project (1979) *Organising Aftercare.* London: The National Corporation for the Care of Old People.
SHEGOG, R. F. A. (1981) *The Impending Crisis of Old Age: A Challenge to* Ingenuity. London: Oxford University Press/Nuffield Provincial Hospital Trust.
SKEET, M. (1971) *Home from Hospital: The Results of a Survey Among Recently Discharged Hospital Patients.* The Dan Mason Nursing Research Committee of the Florence Nightingale Memorial Committee of Great Britain and Northern Ireland.

Integrated Services for the Elderly

ALISON COOPER

As a clinical psychologist, trained in the health service, but now working in a social services department, I hope that I do have a preparedness to see both points of view about difficulties in integrating health and social services. My post is centrally based in the social services department, and I attempt to provide a service both to clients and staff. Consequently, my work involves a fair amount of liaison within the department, between day care, residential, social work and domiciliary services. There are, of course, problems inherent in this, but they have no comparison with problems arising in liaison with entirely different departments.

In my experience, there are two main sorts of service-delivery problem. The first arises when there is a simple shortfall in availability of service. In our area, chiropody and sheltered housing are particular examples. I find that this sort of problem tends to create despair rather than acrimony. The real acrimony arises in the second sort of problem where there is an area of overlap, especially between health and social services. Particular examples here would concern disagreement about responsibility for elderly people who need respite care after an accident which had not resulted in actual injury, and the question is whether they should have an overnight stay in hospital or an old peoples home; and an inability to come to grips with responsibility for care for increasingly infirm and physically dependent residents in old peoples homes, who might be thought to qualify for nursing care.

There seem to be certain necessary conditions for a move towards better co-operation and integration of services to meet the needs of these clients at the boundaries.

The first is coherence within one's own service, knowing what the service can and cannot provide and being specific about unmet needs. Day centre provision for elderly people is an example here — too often it attempts to be all things to all people and fails to do a very good job at anything. Under such circumstances, staff are almost bound to complain that they are not receiving sufficient support from other services.

Coherence is dependent on sensible assessment of client needs. By sensible assessment, I mean to imply collecting only information which is useful and action orientated, not routine and pointless filling in of forms. We can too often ascertain with ease the religion of a client, but with great difficulty the medication they are on! Sensible assessment of client needs leads in turn to the next point.

Coherent referrals to other services. We have found that other services will respond much more readily if we do not overwhelm them with vague requests for help, but ask specific and sensible questions after we have gone as far as we can to elucidate matters with the resources available to us.

A knowledge of what other services can realistically offer is, of course, extremely helpful. This cannot be gained on a one-off visit and it means making liaison with other services a real priority in terms of allocating sufficient time to become familiar with the difficulties that other services experience and what they can do.

Conditions which have not been particularly helpful in my view are joint funding of posts, formal training exchanges, which too often tend to involve a brief visit, and committees.

There is, in my experience, one very specific measure which seems to aid integration very considerably, This consists of employing, in ones own service, personnel who have 'crossed over from the other camp'. In our service, for instance, there are two members of staff who are particularly competent in liaising with medical services. One is an ex-health service doctor who is head of the day centre services for the elderly. The other person is an ex-nursing tutor who works in the advisory section of residential services. These people know how the other organisation works, what its informal systems are and speak its language.

Then, of course, there are people who are by virtue of their appointment 'Janus-faced' such as myself and the hospital based social worker.

Of course, training and experience of a particular service is not enough in itself. In the last analysis, co-operation boils down to the personal qualities of the people involved. Important personal qualities seem to consist of being self-critical and able to admit frailties and being able to accept and give support. In my experience, good liaison arises from goodwill between one or two people who are person-orientated rather service-orientated and who are willing to 'break the rules' who then seek out other like-minded pople. Networks are built up which then may or may not later receive formal recognition.

Lastly, it is perhaps worth commenting that discussion about liaison between services always seems to take place between those who deliver the services rather than involving those who receive them. It is perhaps surprising that we do not make more effort to seek the views of those who are actually caught in the cross-fire, namely the elderly clients themselves.

Behavioural Psychotherapy's Contribution to Psychogeriatric Services

ALISON NORMAN

Everyone who has worked in the field of psychogeriatric care and treatment knows how disintegrated and disorganised service provision is and could recite a litany of causes. They include the basic differences in the administrative and professional structures of housing, health and social services; out-of-date, isolated hospital buildings; inadequate NHS staff and resources; serious shortage of skilled, interested professional leadership in the psychogeriatric field; social services pre-occupation with children; untrained, over-stressed staff in residential homes; and personal refusal to accept responsibility or re-think roles.

Behavioural psychotherapists cannot offer a magical cure to these problems. What they *can* do is promote better integration and better service provision by deliberately using their skills in a wide variety of possible settings to train, to sensitize, to evaluate, to devise programmes of treatment and to enable change to happen. For example:

Training volunteers in counselling

This may be done through one of the counselling agencies run by Age Concern, Cruse and others, or by training sessions with the paid staff of a large Age Concern information/advice centre such as Bob Woods undertook in Newcastle. Such training and subsequent supervision and support can do a great deal, not only to improve the service which is offered, but also to break down the barriers between the voluntary and statutory sectors.

Relatives support groups

One of the worst examples of lack of integration is between family supporters and statutory services. Relatives groups, whether hospital or community based, can do a great deal to enable these barriers to be crossed, but setting them up and running them is a skilled task. It is a task in which psychologists, who are themselves experienced in group work can train and support social workers and community psychiatric nurses who may be rightly hesitant to undertake it without such help.

Day hospital, day centre and day room programmes

All regimes providing care, whether in a residential home, a hospital, a day hospital or a day centre should be basically therapeutic in approach. By that I do not mean non-stop reality orientation and physical jerks, but a programme which is designed to provide a positive, supportive and enjoyable experience. This may range from activities designed to restore the confidence and coping abilities of the functionally ill and encourage their sharing of fears and feelings on the one hand, to companionship, comfort and cuddling with very simple occupation or no occupation at all for very frail and demented elderly people on the other. The point is that good programmes don't just happen. The carers need support and training; they need to be clear about what they are trying to do and how they are trying to do it and what their limitations are. They need help to accept what they can't do as well as to do their best with what they can. You can offer this help.

Individual Treatment

This is of course the core of clinical phychiology, but how extensively; in view of the numbers of mentally ill elderly people, it is possible to use these skills directly? Again, I believe psychologists can do most by taking on a teaching and supporting role. Care and accuracy in assessment techniques, such as the use of rating scales, cognitive tests and detailed recorded observation by nurses and others still leave a great deal to be desired and treatment programmes may be vaguer still. Clinical psychology surely has a great deal to offer psychogeriatrics in clarifying assessment techniques, and helping to set treatment goals, as well as with the planning of individual behavioural therapies for those suffering from anxiety, depression and emotional or behavioural disorder.

Social Psychology

Ann Davies, in an article published in the November 1982 *Ageing and Society*, remarks on the often short-lived nature of attempts to change behaviour in institutions and relates this to the uncomfortable nature of the relationship between experimenter and residents; the implied criticism of the status quo in any effort to induce change; and conflict with deeply ingrained institutional routines and assumptions. We urgently need much more thinking and experiment on the integration of behavioural and social psychology so that it percolates down — in the same way as behavioural approaches to therapy are beginning to percolate — to the basic thinking of many different professions.

There is a very real sense in which psychology is, or could be, a profession which is not supplementary, but *fundamental* to all the professions and occupations, in health, social services and the voluntary sector which are, or should be, involved in psychogeriatrics. What I believe you should be doing is to stop lamenting the disintegrated nature of service provision and start building careful, localised, properly monitored and written-up experiments in relationship with other professionals — with occupational therapists, with nurses of all kinds, with physiotherapists, with volunteer counsellors, with social workers, with the staff of every variety of day centre and day hospital, even with hospital administrators and trades union leaders in the big institutions, not to mention psychiatrists. Your skills are too valuable to be hoarded. They need to be used as seed corn, even at the risk of some of them being misunderstood and mis-used. In that way, I believe clinical and social psychology can make a real contribution to genuine service improvement and growth of mutual professional understanding in the field of psychogeriatrics.

References:

DAVIES, A. D. M. (1982) Research with elderly people in long-term care: Some social and organisational factors affecting psychological interventions. *Ageing and Society, 2.*

Discussion

'The Rising Tide' and other discussion documents have told us loud and clear that great numbers of old people are an increasing strain on wealth and social resources. Such publications outline the problem but do not make it go away. There is still a feeling of waiting with diminishing confidence for *the* answer, *the* solution.

Our theme is the integration of services. What do the various professions offer and how do they confront the urgent issues of professional autonomy, and who does what?

Mapping service provision, there are three models:

   (a) *The Patchwork Quilt,* where areas of function neatly dovetail.
   (b) *Gaps and Overlaps,* in which there are manifold gaps between services and professionals, and also areas of major overlap which generate conflicts of interest.
   (c) *The Ideal,* in which there is a core of knowledge that all professionals concerned with service provision have access to and employ. They also have their specialities, but all tap into the core of knowledge of gerontology and basic facts about the elderly.

This last may come one day, but meanwhile we are all tangled in the web of our aspirations and expectations. The only escape is to focus on the needs of our clients rather than our personal needs and skills. Not 'mine' or 'thine'; but 'ours', clients, volunteers and professionals together.

Meeting old peoples' needs can be problematic when there is disagreement between service-providers and the elderly person about what their needs are. For example, the patient who doesn't want to leave hospital; the old person who doesn't take the medication prescribed for him/her.

These conflicts should be cues to looking questioningly at the situation as a whole. There are usually very good reasons. Reluctance to be discharged from hospital may reflect extreme family tension, grossly unsuitable housing, or simply the fact that 'home' is a very lonely, isolated place. Similarly, poor drug-taking 'compliance' can have complex causes:

Complicated instructions are less likely to be followed reliably.
Misunderstandings arise when old people aren't told, or can't remember the reasons for a particular drug.
A confused person may have no-one to remind them.
Side-effects are sometimes unacceptable.

A positive image of old people is seen as necessary for non-demeaning service provision, but some charities set back this cause by perpetuating the 'poor old soul' stereotype in their fund-raising material.

Increasing service integration implies organizational change. Although the reaction to proposed change can be destructive panic, panic *can* be used constructively and creatively. If people are encouraged to confront *why* they are panicking, it can be used to fuel, not block, change.

Descriptions of 'good-practice' can be forceful formative influences. Unfortunately, many projects are not evaluated or described, and fewer are published because scientific journals discourage descriptive papers. To make findings more accessible they could be summarized in 'checklists' or presented in 'soft-back' versions for more popular publications.

Professionals whose work and experience cross professional and service divisions are well-placed to encourage integration of services.

General Issues in Planning and Developing Services

JOHN HATTERSLEY

I have approached this paper from two points of view. Firstly, I have a background as a behaviourist which will colour what I will say. Secondly, I have worked as a psychologist trying to change systems. This has suggested a simple framework which combines these strands.

CLIENT

	Behavioural Experiment	Person who has a mental handicap	Care giver; supporter	Organisations; social system; service system.
PLANNING — OBSERVATION				
INTERPRETATION				
IMPLEMENTATION — INTERVENTION				
EVALUATION				

On the left of the figure are depicted the stages of a standard 'behavioural experiment' or therapy. Data are gathered through an assessment of the situation and these data are interpreted using the psychological knowledge you bring to bear. This interpretation leads to a choice of intervention which is monitored and evaluated so that it can be modified or maintained to achieve a successful outcome. The first part of this model is equivalent to the planning stage in service development. The second part is the equivalent of the changes which follow from this planning together with a method of evaluating the outcome.

Across the top of the figure are the clients that psychologists have to deal with. Our training often focuses primarily on the person who has a mental handicap as our client. In practice, it is clear that the client we spend most of our time with is the care-giver, either the relatives or staff who support the person who has a handicap. Above this, if we are to help bring about any change at these two levels, we almost always have to do something to help the organisation or the system change.

This model can then be used to help make decisions about various issues, some of which I would like to explore. The following issues are not placed in any priority.

Prevention

We need to ask if it is possible to prevent individuals becoming impaired so that they never become handicapped. Secondly, we need to try to minimise the effect of any impairment which has already occurred. In planning prevention we could look at our three 'clients' in the model and list the things that could be done to enhance both primary and secondary prevention.

Enhancing Skills

This is often talked about as 'teaching' or 'training' the person who has a handicap to improve their skills. I feel the notion of 'enhancing skills' describes more accurately what we do in practice, including changes in stimulus control and the use of prosthetic environments. If we apply the above model to this issue, we can look first at the person who has a handicap as our client and look at some of the things we are familiar with in enhancing their skills. We regularly use techniques such as target setting or Individual Programme Plans for this person. We can, however take the care-giver as the client and this involves looking at the skills they have which are relevant to helping the handicapped person. These skills will almost certainly need enhancing if there is to be a change which will benefit the handicapped person. In turn, it is necessary to look at the organisation or system to ensure that any enhancement of staff skills will be valued and maintained. It is clear that each of the 'clients' depends, to some extent, on each other. This simple model is helpful in operating on what is a very complex set of data.

Philosophy

Almost all of the plans concerning people who have mental handicaps which have been written in the last few years contain a section on philosophy. This is usually used to set the scene for the remainder of the document and usually addresses an 'ideal' against which progress can be measured. The philosophy section usually indicates the way that the service will be labelled. There have been many changes in the way we talk about the service. The World Health Organisation has recently suggested that an individual may have an impairment of some structure (physiological, anatomical; psychological). This may cause them to suffer a disability which prevents them from performing within a normal range in some area. Then, it is possible for this disability to cause the person to be handicapped (Heron and Myers, 1983). Relating this issue back to the model, we can ask of the person who has a mental handicap how are they portrayed to others and how will they come to see themselves? How can we help the person become integrated in our society? This has been selected by the proponents of normalization and the related area of Programme Analysis of Service Systems as one of the key factors in service planning and development (Wolfensberger and Glenn, 1975). With respect to the staff, it is important to discover how the staff talk to, and about, the person who has a handicap and to help them develop approaches which reflect a positive value. At the organisational level there are also important questions which relate to the philosophy. Should there be a greater use of those services which are available to the average citizen, sometimes termed generic services, rather than relying on setting up specialist services which may serve to segregate people who have handicaps from the community?

Teamwork and Management

It is recognised that teamwork is an important factor in meeting the needs of people who have mental handicaps. We need to know for any team what levels they are working at and what needs they are trying to meet. It is important to understand how teamwork can be taught and to find ways of doing this with established teams. In particular, the roles of various professionals must be addressed, either to clarify them or to soften their distinctions with the aim of improving the service to the clients. Many professions have an hierarchical structure which can lead to co-ordination from the top. Delegation of such responsibilities can have a positive effect on making staff take a more personal committed approach. Teamwork needs to be co-ordinated and in planning services, decisions regarding management structure are crucial and need much careful thought.

In Sheffield Health District, there is a declared aim for the services to be managed eventually by the Local Authority. This seems to be based on the assumption that most people who have a handicap are not in special need of health care and are thus most appropriately cared for by the social services.

Communication

Good communication is essential, particularly at a time of change in a service. There must be functioning channels for communications in all directions. This will not guarantee that people will understand every communication, but it should ensure that there is a mechanism for correcting misunderstandings. It should also do much to increase the chances that people will come to 'own' the new ideas and thus support their evolution.

Risk Taking

The person who has a mental handicap must have the dignity that goes with the opportunity to take risks. To achieve this, staff too must feel they can take some risks within a relatively safe and supportive environment. This support can only be given by an organisation that has a system for coping with risk taking. It is easy to develop a policy to ensure that the Authority is protected. Risk taking often demands stepping outside of that which is safe, and policies can be very safe. The Service System must find a way of dealing with this without overprotecting and restricting individual development.

Consultation

Part of the process of communication involves consultation, particularly at the stage of planning services. Very often professionals meet together to decide how a service should develop yet no-one has genuinely consulted with the clients in the first two columns of the model. Some services are making progress to include people or their advocates in specific decisions about an individual's needs, but important planning decisions are still made without a client or advocate in sight. Obviously it will be difficult to ensure true consultation, but if we are to develop services to meet individual needs it must be done.

Maintaining Change

If change is achieved it is critical to build in some way of maintaining it. The evaluation stage of the simple behavioural experiment is partly designed to encourage the area of maintenance. This is recognised as essential in helping an individual who has a handicap to change but it is even more important right across a service system. If service management is to be transferred from Health to Local Authorities, along with resources currently held by Health Authorities, it will be necessary to guarantee that such resources will continue to be available to the specific client group.

Staffing

There are many factors under this heading which must be considered. The level of staffing, appropriate training and retraining for new style services, multi-or inter-disciplinary teamwork, and the implications for training all need careful planning. Perhaps the most taxing problem when considering staffing is the roles of the various groups of staff currently working in the field of mental handicap.

Many of these roles are traditional and are not necessarily compatible with the delivery of a modern service. At a time of radical changes, the informal blurring of professional roles, which has started to occur as a means of meeting the individual needs of people who have handicaps, can become a severe professional threat. Inter-professional rivalry can develop or repeat itself as professions attempt to strengthen their own roles as a means to achieve professional survival.

The model encourages us, for each of the issues raised, to ask questions relevant to each client and to seek answers using the simple behavioural experiment.

There are many other issues which could be added to this list, but I have tried to draw-out some which seem to be critical in the planning and implementation of services. I have suggested a simple model involving a behavioural approach to implementing change which takes account of at least three levels of client.

References:

HERON, A. and MYERS, M. (1983) *Intellectual Impairment: The Battle Against Handicap.* London: Academic Press.

WOLFENSBERGER, W. and GLENN, L. (1975) *Program Analysis of Service Systems: A Method for the Quantitative Evaluation of Human Services.* Third Edition. Toronto: National Institute of Mental Retardation.

Service Delivery to School Leavers

SALLY CHESELDINE

It is six years since the National Development Group (NDG) published Pamphlet 3: 'Helping Mentally Handicapped School Leavers.' It was the briefest of the NDG pamphlets and for the most part consisted of recommendations about the assessment of adolescents prior to leaving school, and the need for continued education and training beyond the age of sixteen years. It concluded that there was an urgent need for a properly planned framework to assess the needs of each young person and to help decide how these could be provided within existing local services. The aim is to prevent unnecessary permanent admission to hospital, and the NDG suggest we cannot achieve this more effectively than by considering school leavers who, more than any age group, are at risk in this effect. To what extent have these recommendations been fulfilled or surpassed? I will describe the service that is provided for school leavers in Oldham as an example of a good, and as yet, still developing service.

The Community Mental Handicap Service in Oldham consists of three core teams, each consisting of social workers, community mental handicap nurses and clinical psychologists. Core Team One deals with services for children from birth, or the time a handicap is first identified, up until school leaving. Core Team Two deals with adults, with special reference to those living on their own or with their families — giving family support. Core Team Three also deals with adults, but with reference to to those living in hostels and community group homes. Both of the adult teams inevitably have contact with training centres and further education provisions. Rather than discuss this arguably arbitrary division of roles, suffice it to say that all three teams are involved to some extent in the service for school leavers.

In describing this service it will perhaps be easiest if I describe what is currently happening to a group of ten young people who are due to leave their special school in the summer of 1984. A series of six, weekly metings is being held, in which the young people themselves, their parents, school teachers, social workers and community nurses get together to look at the alternatives for after school. The specific aims of these meetings are:

1. To prepare parents and young people for the school leavers conference which will take place around October this year. This conference draws together all interested parties for each individual school leaver to discuss specific needs.

2. To familiarise parents and young people with the alternatives available.

3. To visit these establishments and discuss what each offers.

The general purpose is to discuss the services available — not just in terms of ATC's or hostels, but also the use of services in the community.

The options really fall into two categories:

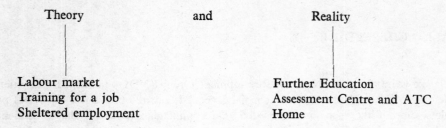

The following diagram gives an overview of the system and its alternative provisions.

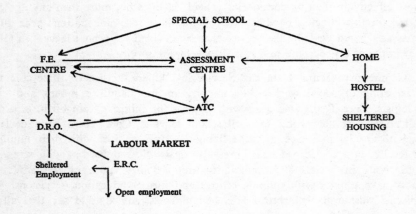

From the special school all go to an assessment centre for one year. In addition to assessing skills, this is very much a social education centre, helping to foster independence and use of community facilities. During this time they may start to attend the Further Education Centre. This is a special provision that has seventeen full-time students, 366 part-timers and 154 members from the local community. So although it comes under Special Education, many of the classes are open to everyone as they would be in any community centre. For this district it is the only community centre. The centre possibly provides the quickest route to the theoretical ideal of the labour market, and there is some, albeit limited, output in this direction. Attendance at the centre is not of a limited duration — a student may continue to attend for as long as he/she remains registered.

For most students, however, the year at the Assessment Centre is followed by an ATC. Yet this should not be taken in an unduly pessimistic way — there is still through-put to the FE centre, and more rarely to the open labour market. Of the ten or so young people leaving school this year one family has declined to take up a place at the Assessment Centre, and has instead opted for their son to work in the family business.

So, in theory there is a service for school leavers. We acknowledge that it is still developing and there are a number of problems as yet to be tackled. We intend having meetings for parents and adolescents throughout the final year to discuss specific problems; for example, leisure and independence. We have not so far followed-up families who have been through this process. A big group of leavers has so far been neglected, namely, the most severely mentally handicapped who may have additional physical handicaps or present behaviour problems. The range of provisions for work skills training, and the prospect of employment is derisory. As with special schools, there is a large catchment area, which leads to problems of transport to the centre, and while young people may learn about facilities in the area of the centre or school this may be of limited value in their own locality. Nevertheless, we feel we have made significant advances in providing a service for mentally handicapped school leavers, and hope that our experiences may be of some benefit to others.

Acknowledgement

I would like to thank Ken Stapleton, Oldham Social Services, for his help in preparing this paper.

References:

NATIONAL DEVELOPMENT GROUP (1977) Pamphlet No. 3: *Helping Mentally Handicapped School Leavers*. London: D.H.S.S.

Teaching Skills to Severely Handicapped Adults in a Residential Setting

PAUL CHAMBERLAIN and MARGARET MULLEN

Mary Rose House was opened in October 1982 as a purpose built locally based hospital unit for 21 long stay and 4 short stay severely mentally handicapped adults. The residents all came from long stay institutional settings and the majority of them have family living and/or have lived themselves in the area in which the house is situated. Given its size, small by hospital standards, but large by private housing standards, considerable effort has been made to make it as domestic and homelike as possible. The residents use all the usual community facilities. If specialist input is required this is provided by the Community Mental Handicap Team. Relatives, friends and volunteers are encouraged to visit and become involved in the daily activities/training.

A qualified person (P.I.C.), supported by two deputies and a number of care staff, is responsible for the day-to-day running of the house. One of the direct care staff has a special responsibility for over-seeing the individual programme planning system. All staff, in addition to skill teaching, carry out all the domestic duties.

Teaching Skills — Background

It is generally accepted that residential units are not the ideal environments for teaching skills to mentally handicapped people. The reasons for this are various and often labelled 'institutional', but in setting up the Mary Rose skill teaching system we kept two thoughts firmly in mind:

1. Institutions are very good at teaching and maintaining behaviour, it is just that they tend to teach and maintain undesirable behaviour in mentally handicapped people.
2. People perform the skills the 'system' demands of them.

Given that a significant number of mentally handicapped people will continue to live in residential units, it is important that we find a way of teaching skills in these buildings under ordinary staffing conditions. The system of skill teaching which is currently being developed is based on individual programme planning principles.

The Skill Teaching System

Direct care staff need to be able to assess accurately, set long and short term achievable goals, write individual programme plans and monitor resident progress, if they are to be successful at teaching skills. We provided a short induction training for the staff. However, we believe that they will learn and generalise the skills if they are shown what to do, practice the skills, and are given immediate positive feedback on their performance by way of close monitoring.

To achieve this we set up a teaching/monitoring system that is built into the operational policy and the routine of the house. This system has a small hierarchy of meetings as its backbone.

(a) *Individual Programme Planning Meeting*

The direct care staff are organised into six groups for individual programme purposes. Each group of three direct care staff assesses/goal sets for three or four named residents. At any one time there is a 1:3 or 1:4 staff/resident ratio. The group meets for approximately one hour once a week with one or two deputy PIC's and the Programme Monitor who is a member of the direct care staff especially selected and given responsibilities for helping to set up and run IPP meetings. In these meetings the group will (1) initiate functional assessments, (2) identify needs and carry out baseline assessments, (3) write IPP's for teaching skills, (4) monitor the progress of these IPP's and (5) identify and carry out baseline assessments of any undesirable behaviours. To assist in these processes we have developed a number of assessments, IPP and monitoring forms which are used exclusively.

50

(b) *Programme Development Meeting*

The group meets once a week and consists of the PIC, the two deputy PIC's, the Programme Monitor, one direct care staff representative and a clinical psychologist. In the meetings, the group will (1) monitor all IPP's and attempt to solve any difficulties, (2) instigate planned interventions for dealing with the assessed undesirable behaviour, (3) monitor and plan residents' reviews and (4) discuss general staff/resident training issues.

(c) *Management Meetings*

The Person in Charge and the two deputies meet once a week to discuss general staff management issues and the day-to-day running of the unit. The general issues are discussed with all the staff once a week.

(d) *Resident Reviews*

On alternate weeks a single resident's progress is reviewed. Parents and all other interested parties are invited to this meeting. The group leader completes a set of progress forms and the action agreed at the meeting is recorded. Each resident is reviewed twice a year.

Results (October 1982 - June 1983)

Behavioural Deficits

Of the 76 baselines kept for behavioural deficits only fifty required further intervention, i.e. the resident was found to possess the skill being monitored. It is possible that the baseline had a 'teaching' effect or that the skills were actually already in the resident's repertoire, but had either not been exhibited during the initial functional assessments or had gradually faded in the resident's previous environment. A variety of self-care, communication and social skills were taught.

Behavioural Excesses

Wherever possible the constructional approach was employed as an intervention. A variety of antisocial and aggressive behaviours were tackled in this way.

Overview of IPP skill teaching system

We would like to think that (1) the staff are performing the skills demanded of them by the system and (2) the system is teaching and maintaining desirable skills in both the residents and staff.

Some Issues

PIC

For new projects the PIC should be identified at least three months before opening. In any case the PIC must be centrally involved in the planning of any skill teaching structure.

Staff

Staff should be selected on their attitudes to the handicapped and their willingness to learn. Induction training gives an orientation but does not teach skills. Ongoing positive monitoring, modelling and the IPP system teaches skills. The involvement of the management staff in this teaching is essential. The career structure of the direct care staff needs examining; currently the best staff tend to leave for higher wage projects.

Admissions

All short and long term admissions should be under the control of the PIC and the small multidisciplinary team who support the unit.

Budgets

It is helpful if the PIC is the budget holder. Clerical assistance and initial support are essential.

Programme Monitoring

The programme monitor is essential for the success of the system. Someone needs to have an on-site responsibility for ensuring the meetings occur and follow a set pattern by being present at them all.

Positive Monitoring

Staff need positive support at all levels. The managers and the small multi-disciplinary team must provide this support for each other if the skill teaching system is going to be allowed to work.

The Ordinary Life Project

JUDY JAMES

Bath, until recently, had virtually no services for families with a mentally handicapped member. Consequently, although having the advantage of not inheriting a vast institution, we started with the disadvantage of a low resource base in terms of money and staffing.

Since 1969 policy papers have laid great emphasis on transferring care out of institutions into communities. The implementation has been disappointingly low. In 1980, The District Planning Team for Mental Handicap, became very interested in the document published by the King's Fund, entitled 'An Ordinary Life', and the

1978 Paper from Campaign for the Mentally Handicapped, 'ENCOR', describing services in Eastern Nebraska. We liked the very simple idea of providing an 'ordinary home-life' as the central core around which many other services must be woven. We decided that we would develop a residential service based on ordinary housing .The Regional Health Authority sees the use of ordinary houses in the community as a natural development of their Locally Based Hospital Unit Policy, and in their recent Regional Plan support the initiatives being taken in Bath. This means that we have the capital monies for acquisition of buildings, but no substantial increase in revenue.

I will describe how the project started, the present structure, and future structure. I will restrict myself to talking about discharging successive groups into ordinary houses in the community, but emphasise that this is in the context of a wider community provision.

The principles underlying the project are those documented in the 'Ordinary Life' Paper:

1. Mentally Handicapped people have the same human value as anyone else and so the same human rights.
2. Living like others within the community is both a right and a need.
3. Services must recognise the individuality of mentally handicapped people.

These ideas had been 'floating' around since 1979 and I think this kind of 'fermentation' period is very necessary. We were, however, faced with the problems of how to start; how to staff; how to fund.

In 1980, a short article by Lowe and Wilkinson appeared in Apex entitled 'A Group Home in Tiverton'. It described how they had discharged four mentally handicapped adults to a group home, with two living-in community service volunteers. The residents were less able than those generally selected for group homes. There was no expectation that they would necessarily live completely independently, and the teaching programmes had been carried out entirely within the home, after leaving hospital.

At that time amongst the population at St. George's hospital, (Bath Health Authority) approximately twenty people were thought to be capable of living in small supervised units within the community.

A staff house belonging to the Authority was vacant and a group was selected. We applied to the Community Service Volunteers Agency in London, for a volunteer who would suit our project. The group was selected: (a) for compatibility, and (b) for skills.

The group moved to a small house attached to the hospital. We had input from the Workers Educational Association. An assessment schedule, the Social Training Achievement Record, was used to assess and define teaching goals. This first group moved out in February 1981 and was remarkably successful. The WEA moved with the residents to the house following through on the training programme and Social Services provided a home help for one morning per week. As they were discharged, they became eligible for non-contributory invalidity benefit and supplementary benefit, and from this they paid their rent.

Using the same model, four further houses have been opened, and we are currently looking for our sixth house. Two houses were formerly staff houses; two were rented commercially and one has been bought.

The amount of support varies according to individual needs. Our most independent group now no longer needs a Community Services Volunteer (CSV), but instead has a person living in, who has a full-time job elsewhere and has no responsibilities for the house other than keeping a 'neighbourly over-sight'. An adult literacy tutor visits for one session; a home help is available one morning per week, and an Occupational Therapy Aide visits one session per week to assist with leisure activities. The most recent group to move out has two CSV's living in, and a care assisstant works twenty hours per week with the group. Some residents attend the local adult training centre, or the community care centre, or attend the hospital's occupational therapy/physio-therapy centre. Most belong to local luncheon clubs and other community organisations.

As the project grew, we found we needed to develop a stronger support system. We used a model similar to the 'Portage' home teaching support system. Each house is allocated a keyworker — this is a member of the nursing staff who spends at least one and a half days per week with a particular household. They provide cover on the CSV's day off, and sleep in if required. They provide continuity when the CSV's change over. They are the 'friends of the household' and provide support and advice to the CSV's.

More recently, a CSV supervisor has taken up post and she provides the counselling, at least one hour per week for each volunteer, which is required by the Volunteer Agency in London. Savings made in closing a ward have been used to develop and improve the Community Service.

The Individual Programme Planning meetings, held fortnightly, provide on-going support training, goal planning and identify gaps in provision. Recently, The Ordinary Life Project Association was formed which will have charitable status. It will be the tenant of the health authority and will take on the day-to-day management of the project.

St. George's Hospital is the support unit for the cluster of ordinary houses, eventually we hope to develop a network of support houses, providing short-term care and back-up support to the community, including the cluster houses, each serving a small geographical catchment area.

The success of the project to date has given us confidence. Each household has developed in its own unique way. Each person has blossomed. They have all developed busy, social lives. It is always a joy to visit each house and to be their guest.

References:

ENCOR — The Way Ahead (1979) London: Campaign for Mental Handicap.

KING'S FUND CENTRE (1980) *An Ordinary Life.* London: King's Fund.

LOWE, N. and WILKINSON, L. J. (1980) A Group Home in Tiverton *Apex, 8.*

Interventions

A. PEOPLE WITH LONG-TERM PSYCHIATRIC DISABILITY

Issues in Assessment

JOHN HALL

This paper will examine the practicalities of carrying out assessments in rehabilitation settings, as well as briefly covering some of the methodological and scientific aspects of assessment. Questions about assessment can be broadly divided into five categories.

A. *Why Assess Anyway?*

Usually when an assessment is asked for in a rehabilitation setting, someone (e.g. direct care staff, other professionals, managers, planners, etc.) is looking for the solution to some question about an individual client or group of clients.

Unfortunately, in most instances one begins with a gross deficiency of knowledge about the client group, as any cursory examination of their case notes will confirm. So, to begin with it is necessary to define more clearly the reasons for the assessment. For example, the purpose of the assessment might be to categorise clients into various groups, and thus answer questions about the types of resources and number of places needed by each group. Other reasons might include the assessment of an individual's needs and identification of target behaviours for a subsequent programme, or the monitoring of changes in clients' behaviour.

Whatever the reason for an assessment, this will to some extent determine the content of the assessment procedure. For example, if an assessment is used to monitor changes in clients' behaviour then care must be taken to exclude items from the assessment which are 'change insensitive'.

Finally, it is always worth considering that it is easy to rush into using complex assessment procedures too soon, and depending on the initial question, it may be that a fairly simple grading system will provide the relevant answers. This is especially true if the assessment is to be applied to very large numbers of clients at the same time.

B. *What to Assess?*

Generally, most assessment procedures focus on current overt behaviour — although the value of knowledge about past behaviour as a predictor of current behaviour should not be underestimated. Current behaviour can be divided into three categories: (a) deficits; Wallace (1976) found that deficit behaviours are the most frequently targeted goals in behavioural rehabilitation programmes. This has caused some to overlook, (b) deviant or excess behaviours, and (c) assets. Obviously these need to be included in any comprehensive assessment; for example, many chronic patients will often have some residual skills/assets which can be built into a programme.

As well as assessing aspects of the person, it is also possible to assess the environment: (i) physical environment, the layout of the ward etc., and (ii) social environment, the rule systems operating in the ward, and the quality and frequency of staff-patient interactions (Wykes, 1982).

Finally, in deciding what to assess we need to consider the criteria for including an item in an assessment. These appear to be (i) frequency of behaviour, frequently occurring deviant behaviours and deficits are most likely to be targeted; (ii) outcome behaviours, the desired outcome behaviours should be included in any assessment procedure (for example, the skills an individual might need for independent community living), and (iii) perceived importance, what the care staff 'see' as important behaviours need to be included.

C. *Who Should Assess?*

In most rehabilitation settings there is little choice over who should assess. It will invariably be the direct care staff and often the least trained staff. For example, on a ward, while the sister or charge nurse are the best suited in terms of skill to carry out an assessment, it is often the learners or nursing assistants who have the most contact with the patients and are thus the most knowledgeable about their behaviour. This must be recognised when designing an assessment procedure, so that its content is easily understood by care staff.

This leads on to the issue of reliability. Hall (1979) found that only 15 out of 225 studies reviewed quoted any reliability figures for their assessments. One reason for this general omission may be the reality that in most wards there is a very low probability, for various reasons, of two staff observing the same client at the same time. Hall found that only 15% of a patient's daily life was even potentially observable by two staff.

Finally, little use has been made of self-report and interview measures with chronic mentally ill clients — surely an omission which needs investigating.

D. *How to Assess?*

There is no doubt that Rating Scales are the most popular form of assessment (Hall, 1979), in preference to complex and time consuming behavioural observation procedures (e.g. Paul and Lentz, 1977). However, few of the published rating scales meet even minimal methodological criteria (Hall, 1980). Given the popularity of rating scales, certain decisions need to be made before applying a particular scale. For example, the time base needs to be considered (i.e. at what intervals will the assessment be carried out?). This will vary according to the purpose of the assessment — if one is using the assessment to monitor change and if change is slow, then the too frequent application of the assessment will fail to adequately demonstrate these changes. This might then have a demoralising effect when fed back to staff. Behavioural methods should similarly be carefully chosen (Haynes, 1978).

E. *Where Assessments Take Place*

With the shift in emphasis from hospital to community care, it is worth considering that any assessment procedure will need to be flexible enough or be adapted for use in a variety of settings. Also, this policy leads to changes in the patient population in the various settings, i.e. they are no longer easily categorised into homogeneous groups. This necessitates the use of specifically tailored assessment procedures.

Conclusion

There are many outstanding issues with regard to the assessment of people with chronic psychiatric disabilities. In addition to those outlined in this paper, questions such as client reactivity to assessments, assessment failures (clients who for various reasons cannot be easily included in an assessment), and the issue of the implicit social norms incorporated into assessment procedures, all need to be dealt with fully. Similarly, we need to know what components of any assessment procedure are the best predictors of successful outcome.

Any intervention with people who have chronic psychiatric disabilities *must* be preceded by a careful assessment of their needs. Therefore if the intervention is to be effective we need to consider the issues surrounding the assessment procedures.

References:
HALL, J. N. (1979) Assessment procedures used in studies on long-stay patients: A survey of papers published in the *British Journal of Psychiatry. British Journal of Psychiatry, 135,* 330-335.
HALL, J. N. (1980) Ward rating scales for long-stay patients: A review. *Psychological Medicine, 10,* 227-288.
HAYNES, S. N. (1978) *Principles of Behavioural Assessment.* New York: Gardner Press.
PAUL, G. L. and LENTZ, R. J. (1977) *Psychosocial Treatment of Chronic Mental Patients.* Cambridge, Mass.: Harvard University Press.
WALLACE, C. J. (1976) Assessment of psychotic behavior. In M. Hersen and A. S. Bellack (Eds.) *Behavioral Assessment: A Practical Handbook.* Oxford: Pergamon Press.
WYKES, T. (1982) A hostel-ward for 'new' long-stay patients. In J. K. Wing (Ed), *Long-Term Community Care: Experience in a London Borough. Psychological Medicine,* Monograph Supplement 2. Cambridge University Press.

Influencing Staff Behaviour

PETER WOODS and PETER HIGSON

Woods and Cullen (1983) looked at possible determinants of the behaviour of staff working with clients in long-term residential care — the mentally handicapped, the elderly and the chronic mentally ill. Commencing with two assumptions (a. the aim of work with long-stay populations includes improving their quality of life, mainly by increasing their adaptive behavioural repertoires, and *b*. what is done by direct care staff and to a lesser extent by other professionals has a profound effect on clients' behaviour), they considered the evidence for the effectiveness of various strategies designed to change staff behaviour in order to bring about changes in clients' adaptive behaviour. They concluded that there was little convincing evidence that traditional approaches such as lectures, workshops, courses and so on were effective in producing long lasting changes in staff behaviour.

They then went on to attempt to isolate the main characteristics of therapteutic interventions with long-stay populations and observed that in most instances the rate of client behaviour change is slow and often imperceptible. In contrast, for any changes to be effected in clients' behaviour, staff behaviour must change relatively quickly and be thus maintained, often for long periods. Moreover, even when there are perceived beneficial changes in residents' behaviour, these do not always appear to be important determinants of staff behaviour. What, therefore, does maintain staff behaviour?

The present paper tries to answer this by examining one of the studies quoted in Woods and Cullen in more detail; a Token Economy Programme (TEP) which has been in operation since 1975 (see Woods, Higson and Tannahill, 1984; for details). The long term data from this programme revealed the existence of two distinct forms of resident behaviour change. For about one-third of the clients, the rate of behaviour change was rapid and was maintained once the contingencies were removed. For these clients the programme could be described as having had a 'therapeutic' effect. In contrast, for the remaining two-thirds the rate of behaviour change was extremely slow, with improvements in behaviour only being observed after years of applying the contingencies. In addition, these improvements disappeared once the contingencies were removed (cf. Woods *et al.*, 1984). For the latter group the programme had a 'prosthetic' function (cf. Lindsley, 1964).

The interesting aspect of this programme in the present context is that staff behaviour did change and has been maintained over a very long period. How was this achieved? Hall and Baker (1973) looked at the possible sources of *breakdown* in TEPs. What, therefore, were the sources of maintenance in this TEP? In retrospect, the following features appear to have been critical to the effectiveness of the programme.

Methodology

We consider that the methodology employed had subtle but powerful effects on staff behaviour. The methodology was that of Applied Behaviour Analysis, of which two aspects seem to have been important:

(i) *Recording Method*. All target behaviours, or the environmental products of such behaviours, have to be directly observed and immediately recorded by the staff on daily charts. The consequences of adopting this methodology are:

(a) It schedules a high number of staff/resident interactions.
(b) It provides a continuous prompt to the staff regarding their own behaviour in relation to the residents. The staff have to observe and consequate residents' behaviour in order to record.

(c) It introduces explicit accountability between grades of staff. The charge nurse has a tangible means of monitoring junior staff performance and can consequate it accordingly.

(d) It provides immediate and accurate numerical feedback to staff concerning residents' behaviour, and thus by implication their own.

Compare this recording method with the one typically employed in British TEPs. In many instances, while the programme contingencies are applied to specific target behaviours, their effectiveness is not measured in terms of *actual* changes in *specific* behaviours, but through the use of some form of behaviour rating scale. These often measure broad categories of behaviour, including different (although generally similar) behaviours to the target behaviours, and are completed at some interval (hours/days) *after* the client has performed the behaviours. The data provided by rating scales therefore is often not behaviourally specific and is separated in time from the occurrence of the behaviours.

(ii) *Reversals*. The periodic removal of treatment contingencies can be used to evaluate the effectiveness of an intervention within a single-subject methodology. These reversals can also prove to be an important source of maintenance. For example, when staff 'feel' that their efforts are not producing effective results, a reversal to non-contingent conditions is often introduced, by consensus agreement, to objectively evaluate effectiveness. The results of such reversals (cf. Woods et al., 1984), can provide 'perceptible' feedback to staff on their own effectiveness. Reversals therefore provide both a means of evaluating clinical effectiveness empirically, *and* feedback that can help to sustain staff behaviour.

Of course, the methodology used in establishing and operating a programme is not in itself sufficient to guarantee changes in staff behaviour. Just as direct care staff behaviour is the major determinant of residents' behaviour, so staff behaviour is to a large extent determined by the behaviour of other professionals within their social environment.

Management

For any therapeutic programme to be effective with residential populations, the aims, objectives and procedures should be fully integrated with the overall management structure of the ward or unit. For example, while staff roles and responsibilities have to be explicitly recognized, the principle of corporate decision making has to be established. All direct-care staff of whatever designation or grade should be fully involved in the decision making process. This has been stated by many other authors (e.g. Hall and Baker, 1973), yet it is surprising how many programmes fail for this reason.

In a hospital based programme probably the most important determinant of staff behaviour, and the most effective means of ensuring that the programme is fully integrated into ward management procedures, is the behaviour of medical staff and nursing officers. Both professions occupy key positions of authority within the hospital system. In the present programme this has been exploited, and efforts have been made to influence their behaviour. As a result, these personnel now make full use of evaluative data from the programme in any decision making, and provide positive and negative consequences for staff compliance with the programme.

This is also the case for other professionals who relate to the unit, although in most hospitals it is probably not such an important determinant of staff behaviour.

Conclusion

There appear to be three main sources of influence on staff behaviour. Training is not, in itself, sufficient to produce long-term changes in staff behaviour. While knowledge and skills are essential, to them must be added long-term changes in the environment which will maintain staff behaviour. We believe that the programme methodology and the behaviour of other professionals are two major contributors to this process.

References:

HALL, J. N. and BAKER, R. D. (1973) Token economy systems: Breakdown and control. *Behaviour Research and Therapy, 11,* 253-263.

LINDSLEY, O. R. (1964) Geriatric behavioural prosthetics. In R. Kastenbaum (Ed.) *New Thoughts on Old Age.* New York: Springer.

WOODS, P. A. and CULLEN, C. N. (1983) Determinants of staff behaviour in long-term care. *Behavioural Psychotherapy, 11,* 4-18.

WOODS, P. A., HIGSON, P. J. and TANNAHILL, M. M. (1984) Token economy programmes with chronic psychotic patients: The importance of direct measurement and objective evaluation for long-term maintenance. *Behaviour Research and Therapy, 22,* 41-51.

Practical Aspects of Working a Joint Hospital and Local Authority Rehabilitation System

COLIN GRIERSON   PATRICK WALLACE
MARK O'CALLAGHAN   TREVOR O'NEILL

This paper concentrates upon practical aspects of achieving close co-operation between hospital and community based rehabilitation units (Middlewood House and Hollymoor Hospital; see paper by O'Callaghan and colleagues). Although system planners can agree on particular joint co-operative aims, it is the staff 'on the ground' who have to find and implement practical ways of achieving them.

One of the major obstacles to co-operation and a potential source of much mis-understandings (and even ill-feeling) between health and social services units is the lack of knowledge about each other's system. One way of overcoming this problem is to adopt similar referral, assessment, training, review, discharge and follow-up processes.

Referral, Assessment and Admission Process

As well as the same Background Information/Referral Form to ease communication, both units have similar information booklets. As a test of motivation clients are invited to apply, since the emphasis is on the client understanding the aims and methods of the unit and expressing a wish to come by filling out the application form at the back of the booklet.

Although separate referrals are directed to either unit, in certain instances (especially with Special Hospital, longer stay or slightly disturbed patients) a joint referral is made whereupon a joint assessment takes place. Thus, a joint planned programme for the client's transition can be made through the rehabilitation unit at Hollymoor Hospital and Middlewood House, the former taking on the first stages of the rehabilitation process, the latter undertaking the second part.

Joint referrals and assessment are also useful in the 'in between cases'. As part of our aim to achieve a complimentary rehabilitation system, Hollymoor Hospital takes those who are more psychiatrically disabled, with Middlewood House helping those whose problems are more socially based. The right blend of help can be devised from the joint assessment without the usual rancour developing of these 'shuttle' cases with attendant charges of 'dumping' and 'creaming'.

The assessment for admission to either unit is done by those most directly involved in the rehabilitation training process, i.e. the nursing or social services staff, with help from other professions if necessary. The client's relatives and any other agencies may also be involved at this stage to enable a fuller picture to be gained of the client's overall circumstances as well as to gain co-operation in training programmes.

Training

At both establishments training is co-ordinated by a key worker who evaluates the overall effectiveness of any training programme, gathers and disseminates relevant information and co-ordinates between the units and with any relevant professionals involved. The key worker also provides individual counselling sessions to the client.

Whilst training techniques are based on learning principles there is a strong emphasis on being as realistic as possible. Community orientated rewards and sanctions apply in both units with the individual taking responsibility for his/her own actions during rehabilitation and afterwards. Thus, extreme anti-social behaviour may lead to the appropriate agency being called (e.g. the police.) Appropriate social behaviour is rewarded by social reinforcement, although in the first stages of certain longer-stay rehabilitees' programmes extra or more tangible consequences may in some cases be necessary (e.g. part funding towards trainee's own organised social outing).

Skills are taught at the most appropriate time, in both group and individual sessions. Thus, work/occupation skills (unless inappropriate) are taught during the day with social and leisure skills being generally trained more in the evening and at weekends, except for those unlikely to be employed. Domestic training occurs mainly in the early morning, evening and at weekends.

Reviews

Reviews are an essential part of any rehabilitation process. They are conducted on a multidisciplinary basis and involve any appropriate agency, including the family. Reviews held at Middlewood may include Hollymoor staff to provide feedback as to progress as well as to learn of any techniques in dealing with difficulties. Similarly, reviews held at Hollymoor may involve Middlewood staff if the client may go there. These also provide a means of linking training to Middlewood more appropriately. Reviews can also act as a forum for practical training of staff at both units.

Discharge and Follow-up

The same Discharge/Leaving Check List is used at both establishments. The aim of this checklist is to ensure that the future placement for the trainee is appropriate and that all adequate resources are available. A monthly formal liaison meeting with the housing department ensures that appropriate council accommodation is supplied to the client. In the case of private accommodation both units adhere to a common written code of practice. Follow up may be provided by staff from either unit with community psychiatric nurse and/or specialist mental health social worker support.

Staff Training

One of the essential elements of any good rehabilitation and continuing care system is the provision of adequate staff in terms both of number and training. With regard to the latter much valuable experience is gained 'on the job' supplemented by joint workshops mounted with the assistance of Birmingham University and local specialist agencies. The highly useful interchange scheme involving staff from each unit working on the other has been running for some time and involves direct training of staff. This helps in sharing resources and enables ideas developed in one unit to be transferred to the other. Joint visits are also arranged to other establishments as part of the training process. Even when educating others the emphasis is on *joint* presentations for it is important that both units share in success as well as in failure.

Finally, a most important way to encourage co-operation 'on the ground' is by joint social events. Monthly meals out are arranged and joint parties are held. Similarly, there is a monthly hostel support group for rehabilitation hostels in the West Midlands where staff meet to exchange ideas and share problems in a social atmosphere.

These then are some of the ways in which close co-operation can be achieved by staff who 'work on the ground'. They are now being extended to include a Birmingham Association for Mental Health hostel, and a joint venture between COPEC Housing Trust and Birmingham Social Services with the aim of spreading closer co-operation in rehabilitation and continuing care even further.

HILTEC Services: A New Perspective in Employment Rehabilitation

CAROLINE SINCOCK and ADRIAN HALLMARK

HILTEC Services is a facility providing temporary work and active employment rehabilitation procedures for individuals who have at some time experienced psychiatric illness.

It comprises two sections, a workshop in which aids for the handicapped are made and designed; and an office in which collation and dissemination of information on leisure services in Greater Manchester is undertaken. There is a workforce of 14 people, 10 in the workshop, 4 in the office and a staff of 6. All individuals are on temporary one year contracts.

This type of provision is relatively new and HILTEC Services has developed as a result of the following.

Firstly, there is a body of knowledge which documents that individuals who are unemployed experience psychological deterioration (Jahoda, 1979: Harrison, 1976; Shepherd 1981). The Government through the development of the community programme has set up schemes to try and ameliorate many of the effects of unemployment on an individual.

Secondly, obtaining work after psychiatric illness is very difficult because of the problems of employer prejudice, incomplete work histories and loss of self-confidence. HILTEC Services provides individuals with a period of employment (up to one year), aims to increase their confidence and helps with regard to employer prejudice.

Thirdly, Employment Rehabilitation Centres have changed to meet changing client needs. Their clients are now more likely to have a variety of difficulties, primarily related to psychological or psychiatric rather than physical disabilities. The Employment Rehabilitation Centres at Egham and Leicester have been particularly useful regarding the development of HILTEC.

Finally, in 1981, there was a review of employment rehabilitation resulting in the recommendation of provision of employment rehabilitation facilities by voluntary bodies under the community programme scheme. HILTEC Services is an example of such a scheme.

HILTEC Services combines the following factors:

(a) An extended period of work habituation (up to one year).
(b) Individual assessment of practical and work related skills.
(c) Emphasis on goal setting, feedback and development of work skills.
(d) A range of practical work skills.
(e) The opportunity to earn a realistic wage.

A three-stage selection procedure is used. Firstly, the completion of a job application form, secondly an interview and thirdly a period of work assessment. The aim of the first two is to obtain information concerning the individual's mental state, social and employment history and motivation to obtain employment. The third stage identifies skills and deficits within a work environment, and this information forms the basis for the goals of rehabilitation.

The validity and effectiveness of HILTEC Services as an employment rehabilitation facility is being evaluated. A number of factors are assessed in addition to the final outcome measure of placement in open employment. These are:

(a) The individual's mental state (The General Health Questionnaire; Goldberg, 1972).

(b) Practical work skills and work related skills, e.g. attendance and interaction with colleagues. (The Griffiths Standardised Assessment of the Work Behaviour of Psychiatric Patients; Griffiths, 1973).

(c) The psychosocial environment of the workshop (The Social Climate Scale; Cornes and Horne, 1981).

These measures are being administered to the workers at three monthly intervals, and, excluding the General Health Questionnaire, will also be given to comparable control subjects from E.R.C. and I.T.U. populations. A follow up questionnaire will be sent to all subjects one year following termination of their courses to ascertain whether or not they have found employment, its nature and duration.

At the time of writing this paper too little data has been collected to draw any firm conclusions regarding HILTEC Services as an employment rehabilitation facility. However, the data at this time indicate that the population as a whole are functioning at a lower level than that considered suitable for open employment, and both the workers and staff perceive the environment of HILTEC to be appropriate for an employment rehabilitation facility.

Clearly, further results are needed to make any realistic judgement about HILTEC Services as a rehabilitation facility. Over the past nine months staff recruited from the long-term unemployed have been able to cope with many of the problems presented by people at HILTEC. Their skills in goal setting have developed and they are able to deal with day to day issues confidently. However, it has become apparent that further input is required regarding the management of behaviour, identification of changes in health and the appropriate services to contact. These difficulties should be lessened by the provision of, in the next year of the project, a community care worker and more detailed staff training and support for the supervisors.

References:

CORNES, P. and HORNE, D. (1981) The measurement of rehabilitation centre social climates. *Journal of Occupational Psychology, 54,* 289-297.

GOLDBERG, D. P. (1972) The Detection of Psychiatric Illness by Questionnaire Maudsley Monograph No. 21. London: Oxford University Press.

GRIFFITHS, R. D. P. (1973) A standardised assessment of the work behaviour of psychiatric patients. *British Journal of Psychiatry, 123,* 403-408.

HARRISON, R. (1976) The demoralizing experience of prolonged unemployment. *Department of Employment Gazette, 84,* 339-348.

JAHODA, M. (1979) The impact of unemployment in the 1930's and the 1980's. *Bulletin of the British Psychological Society, 32,* 309-314.

MANPOWER SERVICES COMMISSION (1981) *Employment Rehabilitation: A Review of the M.S.C. Employment Rehabilitation Services.* London: M.S.C.

SHEPHERD, G. (1981) Psychological disorder and unemployment. *Bulletin of the British Psychological Society, 34,* 345-348.

Intervention with Families with a Schizophrenic Relative: A Move towards Psychological Management of Acute Schizophrenia in the Community

NICHOLAS TARRIER and CHRISTINE BARROWCLOUGH

Community care for people suffering from schizophrenia supposedly began during the 1950's with the use of neuroleptic medication and a change in policy away from long-term institutionalisation. However, inadequate financing for community based care and a remaining high frequency of relapse and re-admission of patients suffering from schizophrenia have apparently prevented this policy from being realised in practice. Evidence suggests that the new long-stay population is in fact increasing (Wooff, Freeman and Fryers, 1983). It is estimated that 30-40 per cent of patients receiving medication will relapse within one or two years (Leff and Wing, 1971; Johnstone, 1976) and about 7% would not respond at all (Leff and Wing, 1971). Long-term success at improving community care would appear to lie with identifying factors that precipitate relapse in acute schizophrenia as it is these factors that start acute patients on their career to becoming chronically disabled.

The problem does not appear to be a purely medical one of disease process, and extensive research has been carried out investigating the role of environmental determinants of relapse in schizophrenia. Research from the MRC Social Psychiatry Unit over the last 20 years has produced important advances in our knowledge of precipitants of relapse, and has initiated intervention projects aimed at keeping people well, and functioning in the community.

One factor that has been found to be important in precipitating relapse is the emotional climate of the home. This emotional climate has been assessed by use of the Camberwell Family Interview (Brown and Rutter, 1966) from which relatives were categorised as being high or low on Expressed Emotion (E.E.) depending on the amount of criticism, hostility or emotional over-involvement elicited during the interview. Patients returning to high E.E. relatives had a higher relapse rate during a 9 month follow-up period (58%) than patients returning to low E.E. relatives (16%), (Brown, Birley and Wing, 1972). Further studies confirmed this relationship (Leff and Vaughn, 1981; Vaughn, Snyder, Freeman, Jones, Falloon and Liberman, 1982). It was further found that patients living with high E.E. relatives could use two protective strategies, taking regular medication or having low face-to-face contact with their relatives. If both strategies were implemented then relapse rates were quivalent to those with low E.E. relatives, otherwise relapse rates were very high (92%).

These studies were very important. Firstly they demonstrated consistently the interaction between environmental and biological factors. In support of this, psycho-physiological studies have demonstrated differing levels of autonomic arousal in patients in the presence of their relatives depending on whether the relative was high or low E.E. (Tarrier, Vaughn, Lader and Leff, 1979; Tarrier and Barrowclough,

1983a). These differences appeared environmentally determined and were not due to intrinsic differences in the patients (Tarrier and Barrowclough, 1983a). The psychological mechanisms that are mediating E.E. and the patients' responses are at present obscure, but there is some suggestion that the relatives' emotional distress and perceived inability to cope may be important (Tarrier and Barrowclough, 1983a). A second important outcome of the expressed emotion studies has been the ability to identify patients at 'high risk' due to environmental factors. This has allowed intervention methods to be directed at modifying these factors and reducing risk.

Social intervention studies are not new but have been previously so methodologically flawed by, for example, problems regarding diagnosis, relapse criteria and operationalisation of intervention that few conclusions could be made (Klein, 1980; Tarrier and Barrowclough, 1983b). Two recent studies are, however, much more promising. The first by Leff and colleagues (1982) selected patients at 'high risk' in having high E.E. relatives with whom they had high contact. The intervention package of an educational programme, relatives' groups and family therapy was aimed to reduce the relatives E.E. and/or contact and hence to reduce relapse compared to routine outpatient treatment. All patients were on medication. At 9 months the family intervention group had only 9% relapse compared to 50% of the control group.

Although methodologically and conceptually a great improvement on previous studies the intervention methods in this study are poorly operationalised making replication difficult and identification of 'active ingredients' impossible. The second study was carried out by Falloon and his colleagues (1982) in California. The intervention was a behavioural problem-solving approach to dealing with intra-and extra-familial stress. A family therapy group was compared to an individual therapy group again with considerable success. Relapse, active symptoms and perhaps surprisingly medication levels being significantly reduced in the family intervention group. An advantage of Falloon's work over his English colleagues is the emphasis placed on improved social functioning of the patient and problem-solving skills of the family, as opposed to purely reducing relapse rates.

In conclusion, then, we can have a certain optimism that it is possible to produce intervention packages that can be implemented cost-effectively as part of community after-care programmes to help discharged acute patients and their families cope with and reduce environmental stresses. These interventions should be aimed not only at reducing relapse and symptomatology but also at increasing levels of positive functioning. However, non-specific effects and 'active ingredients' need to be investigated in future research (Tarrier and Barrowclough, 1983b).

References:

BROWN, G. and RUTTER, M. (1966) The measurement of family activities and relationships: A methodological study. *Human Relations, 19,* 236-241.

BROWN, G., BIRLEY, J. and WING (1972). Influence of family life on the course of schizophrenic disorders: A replication. *British Journal of Psychiatry, 121,* 241-258.

FALLOON, I., BOYD, J., McGILL, C., RAZANI, J., MOSS, H. and CILERMAN, A. (1982) Family management in the prevention of exacerbations of schizophrenia. *New England Journal of Medicine, 306,* 1437-1440.

JOHNSTONE, D. A. W. (1976) The duration of maintenance therapy in chronic schizophrenia. *Acta Psychiatrica Scandinavia, 53,* 298-301.

KLEIN, D. (1980) Psychosocial treatment of schizophrenia, or psychosocial help for people with schizophrenia. *Schizophrenia Bulletin, 6,* 122-130.

LEFF, J. and WING, J. (1971) The trial of maintenance therapy in schizophrenia. *British Medical Journal, 3,* 599-604.

LEFF, J. and VAUGHN, C. (1981) The role of maintenance therapy and relative's expressed emotion in relapse of schizophrenia: A two year follow-up. *British Journal of Psychiatry, 139,* 102-104.

LEFF, J., KUIPERS, E., BERKOWITZ, R., EBERLEIN-VRIES, R. and STURGEON, D. (1982). A controlled trial of social intervention in the families of schizophrenic patients. *British Journal of Psychiatry, 141,* 121-134.

TARRIER, N. and BARROWCLOUGH, C. (1983a) Psychophysiological assessment of expressed emotion in schizophrenia: A case example. (submitted for publication).

TARRIER, N. and BARROWCLOUGH, C. (1983b) Psychosocial intervention and its effect on the course of schizophrenia: A review. (submitted for publication).

TARRIER, N., VAUGHN, C., LADER, M. and LEFF, J. (1979) Bodily reactions to people and events in schizophrenics. *Archives of General Psychiatry, 36,* 311-315.

VAUGHN, C., SNYDER, K., FREEMAN, W., JONES, F., FALLOON, I. and LIBERMAN, R. (1982) Family factors in schizophrenic relapse. Schizophrenia *Bulletin, 8,* 425-426.

WOOFF, K., FREEMAN, H. and FRYERS, T. (1983) Psychiatric service use in Salford: A comparison of point prevalence ratios 1968 and 1978. *British Journal of Psychiatry, 142,* 588-597.

B. THE ELDERLY

Problem-Solving Groups for the Elderly

GEOFF GARLAND

As Burnside (1978) suggests, an unstructured therapeutic group can be diffuse and of doubtful effectiveness. Indeed, the complex input generated by such a group is likely to be particularly unsuitable for clients who, for reasons summarised by Knox (1977) already have reduced problem-solving capacity.

A possible solution proposed by Rose (1977) is to keep to relatively limited topics, for example, with elderly and/or chronic patients in institutional care, to concentrate on: performance of tasks and decision-making; social skills training or preparation for leaving the institution, (although it seems clear that in practice these topics can overlap).

In Rose (1980) there is brief discussion of a few studies of middle-aged and elderly subjects in small groups working within a cognitive-behavioural approach, to achieve specific improvements. A common factor appears to be careful attention to what Emery, Hollon and Bedrosian (1981) describe as 'treatment socialization' using an educational model of therapy as a systematic way to learn more effective strategies for coping with ageing. Typically, individual homework assignments are an integral part of such groups.

Over the past 5 years at Oxford geriatric and psychogeriatric centres an approach to using small, problem-solving, groups (usually 5 attenders and 2 facilitators meeting once a week for 45 minutes over 12 weeks), has been evolving, guided by the above considerations.

Potential members are individually screened for ability to communicate without major difficulty and to present a history including one or more discrete psychological problems, and invited to join the appropriate group. Of those referred, 90% have been invited and there has been 95% acceptance. 12% of attenders leave before 12 weeks and, after excluding these, the groups' dropout rate is 8% (tending to be those who are physically restless, wanting to go home, and denying the centre has any relevance for them).

For the first 4 weeks we build up a group identity using resources to hand. For example, G decided to bring her astrological calendar to share sun sign information with the group, a colourful and successful way of involving us. Shared themes increase group attraction: J reports that he feels more 'lost' than usual today and that the centre looks unfamiliar, and the others hear him out and share with him their own experiences of feeling lost and the resolution of these feelings.

During this time members are generally visited at home, information about function-ing at the centre is collected, history is cross-checked and problems named at screening are gone into and their nature classified, (frequently new issues emerge in their place, or the original ones change almost beyond recognition). Homework, usually to prepare a clear description of a problem, is completed to facilitators' satisfaction 70% of the time.

In weeks 5 and 6 the group concentrates on a specific problem and solution for each member, including one of the facilitators. Solutions are often group ones. For example: W complained that she forgot her handbag, accused others of taking it, became unpopular — what could she do? The group rapidly produced an effective solution. However, D, who feels guilty because she 'shouldn't feel lonely', took several weeks before she could even question her assumption seriously and began to contemplate a solution to her essential problem — how to make the visits of her son and main supporter more rewarding for both parties.

Some problems turn out to be essential in another sense. One category with which we have been unsuccessful is the 'shall I move house or shall I stay where I am?' dilemma. We have come to feel that this type of problem expresses a pervasive uncertainty, and relates to supporters' needs more than the clients', and that we have been unwise to expect resolution in the context of these groups.

From weeks 7-12 progress is reviewed and solutions modified if necessary. Excluding drop-outs, 89% of members are working on a problem by week 7, 78% of these have arrived at a solution by week 12. Of 20 'graduates' reviewed at 3 months, 15 reported no further serious concern with the original problem.

Some groups have been continued beyond a 12-week span and there is usually a desire by members to keep on meeting. It is rare for a group to become fully autonomous for more than 4-6 weeks, partly because attendance for any individual is likely to be disrupted by a variety of factors.

References:

BURNSIDE, I. M. (1978) (Ed.) *Working with the Elderly: Group Processes and Techniques.* London: Duxbury Press.
EMERY, G., HOLLON, S. D. and BEDROSIAN, R. C. (1981) (Eds.) *New Directions in Cognitive Therapy.* New York: Guilford Press.
KNOX, A. B. (1977) *Adult Development and Learning.* San Francisco: Jossey-Bass.
ROSE, S. D. (1977) *Group Therapy: A Behavioural Approach.* New York: Prentice Hall.
ROSE, S. D. (1980) (Ed.) *A Casebook in Group Therapy: A Behavioural-Cognitive Approach.* New York: Prentice-Hall.

Memory Therapy with The Elderly

NICK MOFFAT

This paper proposes the continued development of memory therapy with the elderly, including the confused elderly.

The first concept that requires classification is whether memory complaints and any impaired memory performance might be attributable to stereotypes of forgetfulness amongst the elderly, and hence a reduction in the expectation and requirements for remembering. Langer, Rodin, Beck, Weinman and Spitzer (1979) tested this assumption by rewarding elderly nursing home residents with interpersonal or practical incentives for finding out and remembering information by the time of the next interview. As predicted the experimental groups improved compared with the control conditions on the specific items requested, and on such generalization tasks as short-term memory tests, and ratings of alertness, mental activity and social adjustment. Furthermore, Zarit (1979) attributed much of the value of his memory therapy groups to the reassurance offered to the healthy elderly subjects that their occasional memory failures need not be attributed to impaired memory.

Although the above-mentioned studies recognise the importance of making up for any previous lack of practice at remembering, this is unlikely to fully account for age differences in memory performance. Furthermore, repeated practice has not proved beneficial in improving the memory performance of amnesics, (Brooks and Baddeley, 1976) despite its face validity and popularity as a memory training procedure (Harris and Sunderland, 1981).

The second concept to be examined is the use of memory strategies amongst the elderly. Firstly, it has been found that older subjects may be as good as if not better than younger subjects at estimating their ability on experimental tasks (Perlmutter, 1978). In addition, the younger and older subjects shared an equivalent knowledge of memory, and reported similar strategy use in everyday activities. Secondly, Perlmutter (1978) and Lachman and Lachman (1980) found that their elderly subjects did not show any age decrement in memory for facts. Since the elderly subjects were not impaired on this task they either had intact ability to retrieve this kind of information or were able to infer the correct answer by reference to their store of world knowledge. It is argued that memory for facts may be closely associated with everyday memory requirements.

Utilising the above-mentioned set of skills it may be possible to help piece together information lost from short-term memory. Thus, if an older person has no recollection of having had breakfast, it may be more appropriate to help that person infer that breakfast had been consumed by acknowledging that it is now 10 a.m., and breakfast is always at 8.30 a.m., rather than attempt to cue the actual event (e.g. don't you remember, you had a boiled egg?).

Furthermore, rather than attempt to learn new information it may be more appropriate for certain older individuals to make use of external aids such as notebooks and diaries. For example, Kurlychek (1983) successfully trained a man with mild pre-senile dementia to check his written time-table every time his alarm watch sounded. This resulted in increased self confidence and an ability to attend scheduled sessions without assistance from others.

I used a checklist approach with a man with pre-senile dementia, who was concerned about repeatedly losing things around the house. The possible locations in the house where he might have left his brightly coloured bag, containing his pipe and other possessions, were provided in a flow-chart which guided his search. This proved moderately successful in reducing the repeated questioning of his family about where he had left things, which they had found particularly irritating.

In addition to utilising external memory aids, the benefits of internal memory aids can be considered. A number of the memory strategies rely upon visual imagery, which has proved beneficial for normal and some brain-damaged subjects. However, with the elderly the results have been mixed, perhaps because of an age-related decline in the capacity to deal with visual information (Winograd and Simon, 1980). Thus, although visual imagery techniques may be beneficial under certain circumstances (Robertson-Tchabo, Hausman and Arenberg, 1976) verbal memory strategies may be more appropriate with the elderly, since verbal skills are generally well retained with advancing years. For example, it may be that poor story recall especially for key items (Cohen, 1979) could be improved by organisational strategies (Glasgow, Zeiss, Barrera and Lewinsohn, 1977); although just being able to read the passage rather than listen to it may be beneficial for the elderly (Meyer, Rice, Knight and Jessen, 1979).

First letter cueing, a further verbal memory strategy, proved of considerable assistance in aiding the recall of dementia subjects using experimental materials (Morris, Wheatley and Britton, 1983). It should be possible to incorporate this strategy in practical memory therapy, such as the learning of people's names (Jaffe and Katz, 1975); or in the demonstration of learning taking place before this is detected under free recall or other cueing conditions. This may encourage the elderly client and the therapist to persevere with training.

Certainly, memory therapy can be time consuming and laborious, and therefore it is important to choose information which the client wishes to remember. Furthermore, the selection of an appropriate training routine is also crucial. This should allow for suitably spaced sessions and provide regular probes of memory performance during each session. Gradually retention can be tested over increasingly longer intervals as learning occurs.

In conclusion, it is suggested that memory therapy can be of benefit, particularly when the person's assets and deficits are taken into account in the remediation programme.

References:

COHEN, G. (1979) Language comprehension in old age. *Cognitive Psychology, 11,* 412-429.

GLASGOW, R. E., ZEISS, R. A., BARRERA, M. and LEWINSOHN, P. M. (1977) Case studies on remediating memory deficits in brain damaged individuals. *Journal of Clinical Psychology, 33,* 1049-1054.

HARRIS, J. E. and SUNDERLAND, A. (1981) A brief survey of the management of memory disorders in rehabilitation units in Britain. *International Rehabilitation Medicine, 3,* 206-209.

JAFFE, P. G. and KATZ, A. N. (1975) Attenuating anterograde amnesia in Korsakoff's psychosis. *Journal of Abnormal Psychology, 84,* 559-562.

KURLYCHEK, R. T. (1983) Use of a digital alarm chronograph as a memory aid in early dementia. *Clinical Gerentologist 1,* 93-94.

LACHMAN, J. L. and LACHMAN, R. (1980) Age and the actualisation of world knowledge. In L. W. Poon, J. L. Fozard, L. S. Cermak, D. Arenberg, and L. W. Thompson, (Eds.) *New Directions in Memory and Aging.* New Jersey: Lawrence Erlbaum Associates.

LANGER, E. J., RODIN, J., BECK, P., WEINMAN, C., and SPITZER, L. (1979) Environmental determinants of memory improvement in late adulthood. *Journal of Personality and Social Psychology, 37,* 2003-2013.

MEYER, B. J. F., RICE, G. E., KNIGHT, C. C. and JESSEN, J. L., (1979) Effects of comparative and descriptive types on the reading performance of young, middle and old adults. *Research Report No. 7, Prose Learning Series.* Tempe: Department of Educational Psychology, Arizona State University.

MORRIS, R., WHEATLEY, J., and BRITTON, P. (1983) Retrieval from long term memory in senile dementia: Cued recall revisited. *British Journal of Clinical Psychology, 22,* 141-142.

PERLMUTTER, M. (1978) What is memory aging the aging of? *Developmental Psychology, 14,* 330-345.

ROBERTSON-TCHABO, E. A., HAUSMAN, C. P., and ARENBERG, D. (1976) A classical mnemonic for older learners: A trip that works! *Educational Gerentology, 1,* 215-226.

WINOGRAD, E., and SIMON, E. W. (1980) Visual memory and imagery in the aged. In L. W. Poon, J. L. Fozard, L. S. Cermak, D. Arenberg and L. W. Thompson, (Eds.). *New Directions in Memory and Aging.* New Jersey: Lawrence Erlbaum Associates.

ZARIT, S. H. (1979) Helping an aging patient to cope with memory problems. *Geriatrics,* April, 82-90.

Coping with Physical Handicap in Old Age

CHARLES TWINING

A recent paper by Arie and Jolley (1982) has suggested that, 'psychology has not yet established itself as a regular contributor to psychogeriatric services'. This is almost certainly no longer true. However, this statement could still be made about the contribution of psychology to geriatric medicine.

The aim of this paper is to suggest how the application of behavioural techniques may help elderly people with physical disease or handicap.

Psychological Problems in Geriatric Medicine

A recent paper by Murphy (1982) found that the rate of chronic health problems to be higher in a group of previously undiagnosed depressed elderly people at home than in either non-depressed old people or even those referred to a psychiatric service with depression. This suggests not only that emotional distress is commonly found among the physically frail elderly but that it is often unrecognised as abnormal. It is not yet clear whether to conclude that 'after all she has a lot to be depressed about' is appropriate sympathy or therapeutic nihilism. However it seems reasonable to assume *a priori* that good adjustment means more than being appropriately unhappy.

There are many studies showing that a severely handicapping condition such as a stroke, is often associated with psychological distress both for the patient and for his or her carer (Robins, 1976). Our own studies have indicated that at any one time about 10% of acute geriatric medical patients and 20% of geriatric rehabilitation patients are being prescribed an antidepressant on the ward.

However, there are many other problems that arise in geriatric medicine which may benefit from a behavioural approach. The presenting problem may be lack of behaviour in the patient who has 'given up'. The absence of achievable goals and adequate re-inforcers may be important here. This may also be the origin of difficulties for those who fail to achieve functional progress after physical recovery.

In such cases some cognitive restructuring may be helpful and certainly seems to be necessary in problems of symptoms of 'unknown origin'. Difficulties in distinguishing between symptoms of anxiety and cardiovascular disorder can lead to repeated admission. Behavioural analysis can both clarify matters for the patient and justify further investigation where approrrpriate.

Carers, both relatives and staff, can usefully adopt behavioural methods and often it is they who are the most appropriate target for help.

Developing Strategies

Obviously some approaches to helping the elderly transfer readily from other settings, especially when the major features are of, for example, prolonged institutionalisation rather than age *per se*.

However, the elderly are not all like chronic schizophrenics or the mentally handicapped. Therefore we should consider what kind of changes in our behavioural strategies might be appropriate.

1. *Assessment*

A recent work on 'Behavioural Assessment in Geriatrics' (Herman and Barnes, 1982) includes reference to the M.M.P.I. and projective techniques. These seem to have little practical value in helping elderly Welsh people! More helpful are techniques of time and event sampling, and age is no bar to keeping useful and meaningful records of one's behaviour. I think we have yet to establish whether some techniques are more acceptable than others (for example, analogue versus discrete scales), but this must be done.

In observing behaviour it is already clear that the covert is going to be as important as the overt (Simpson, Woods and Britton, 1981). Residential care may look boring but some residents do not find it so. We must not prejudge.

Assessments must be wide ranging so as to include the multiple problems and individual strengths which characterise the elderly.

2. *Management*

It is generally assumed that techniques must be adapted or shortened for use with the elderly. This may be so but we should check whether this is the case. Certainly some techniques, for example in relaxation training, may be difficult for the arthritic and a soft soothing voice may be inaudible to the hard of hearing.

Clearly, goals have to be set in relation to individual limitations. However one important step for some people is to get them to raise their expectations. Some elderly people as well as their carers all to easily resign themselves to chronic infirmity.

We will need to consider what are the reinforcers for each individual. Generally, ageing is associated with increased variability. We should not assume that this is any less true of learning parameters. An activity like attending a day centre may be a powerful reinforcer to the socialite but a punishment to the recluse.

3. *Research*

The variability of old people suggests that single case designs may be especially appropriate. Subjects must be adequately described to enable appropriate generalisations to be made and in changing conditions (e.g. stroke or dementia) adequate follow-up is essential.

Conclusions

As a foundation for developing these strategies we must not hesitate to find out directly what are the real problems of the physically frail elderly. We must not make stereotyped assumptions about the clients, their carers or the efficacy of our techniques. It would be unhelpful to elderly people and rightly bad for behavioural therapists, if they were to presume how things should be done without first finding out how they are done.

However, it is my firm belief that, as has been shown for other disadvantaged groups, behavioural techniques hold much promise for the physically ill elderly. This is a group who will not get better if we do nothing. The problems are complex and yet their solution must surely be a challenge which behaviour therapists can no longer ignore.

References:

ARIE, T. and JOLLEY, D. (1982) Making services work: Organisation and style of psychogeriatric services. In R. Levy and F. Post (Eds.), *The Psychiatry of Late Life*. Oxford: Blackwell.

HERMAN, S. and BARNES, D. (1982) Behavioural assessment in geriatrics. In F. J. Keefe and J. A. Blumenthal (Eds.), *Assessment Strategies in Behavioural Medicine*. New York: Grune and Stratton.

MURPHY, E. (1982) Social origins of depression in old age. *British Journal of Psychiatry, 141*, 135-142.

ROBINS, A. H. (1976) Are stroke patients more depressed than other disabled subjects? *Journal of Chronic Diseases, 29*, 479-482.

SIMPSON, S., WOODS, R. T. and BRITTON, P. G. (1981) Depression and engagement in a residential home for the elderly. *Behaviour Research and Therapy, 19*, 435-438.

The Adaptive Use of Reality Orientation

BOB WOODS

If Reality Orientation (RO) can be used adaptively, maladaptive uses can also be identified. For example, Gubrium and Ksander (1975) observed its inflexible, mechanical and unthinking use in an American nursing home.

It is easy to criticise RO if it is equated with this sort of mechanical repetiton of day and date, or if RO sessions are seen as the major component of RO, rather than as supplementary to the 24 hour or informal RO approach. Not surprisingly, relatively brief group sessions do not generally change the severely impaired behaviour of demented people outside the group setting (Powell-Procter and Miller, 1982; Burton, 1982). It is, however, premature to write off RO — no published study has shown that 24 hour RO has actually been implemented, let alone measured its effects! The aim here is not to criticise or caricature RO, but to show how it could be a stepping-stone to better practice.

Using the Demented Person's Limited Learning Ability

RO research has provided evidence that people with dementia have some learning ability, which with appropriate training, can be channelled into constructive learning. Greene, Nicol and Jamieson (1979) report 3 single-case studies showing that twice-daily, structured re-orientation sessions in a day-hospital led to a clear increase in verbal orientation. Some generalisation was noted outside the sessions; this was most evident where cognitive skills were examined, but less apparent in social behaviour. Woods (1983) using a multiple baseline design in a single-case study again showed how verbal orientation items could be learned with specific training. A further day-hospital study showed an increase in verbal orientation, with some concomitant changes in both the patients' and the relatives' mood at home (Greene, Tinsbury, Smith and Gardiner, 1983).

Several studies have shown that ward orientation can similarly be taught; some dementing patients *can* learn their way on the ward (Hanley, McGuire and Boyd, 1981). Studies which have compared the usefulness of placing signs around the ward and actual training, suggest that the combination of signs *plus* training is most effective (Hanley, 1981; Gilleard, Mitchell and Riordan, 1981). Staff need to actively point out the signs to the patient. Signs need to be large and clear, combining words and pictures where possible. Symbolic signs are often little help — the picture should be of the object from the normal viewing angle.

The success of RO in these two areas suggests that the dementing person's limited learning ability could be harnessed in whichever areas of functioning are of particular importance for each individual patient.

Intrinsic Basic Attitudes Encouraged by RO

Informal RO involves a number of attitudes which are of value in humanising care, whether or not they 'work' in the narrow sense of producing generalised behavioural change (Holden and Woods, 1982).

It aims to help dementing people experience success. Rather than exposing deficits, questions are framed so that the person can answer appropriately, e.g. cues and prompts might be given, or the answer supplied by the context, or by use of a memory aid. Tasks are set at a level where the person will not fail, with just sufficient help given for the person to be able to complete the task themselves.

RO allows and encourages individuality, dignity, self-respect and choice. This process is assisted if communication with the dementing person can be improved. RO suggests several ways of doing this — using cued recall, having a concrete focus for the conversation (e.g. an object or picture), using visual or auditory materials to elicit and stimulate reminiscence, drawing from the person's store of memories. As staff get to know the person's past life better, often it is easier to make sense of what the person is saying, and it becomes easier to see the patient as a whole person.

RO emphasises that communication should always be attempted, explanations always given, that 'care' should never be silent or done to the person as if they were an object. Even if the explanation is apparently immediately forgotten or seems not to have been understood, something (perhaps at a non-verbal level) may get through.

Effects of RO on Staff

Finally, RO has a number of potentially beneficial effects on staff. It gives a structure to follow and guidelines to use as a yardstick against which to compare current practices. It can be a means of communicating generally accepted ideas about the care of dementing people to those who are less experienced. A number of training aids are available to help with this.

RO encourages staff to get to know the dementing person as a *person*, which both improves the quality of care and increases job-satisfaction. It encourages questioning of the sort of reality we are providing. Is it worth being orientated to this environment? How can the reality be improved and enriched so RO is worthwhile? Often a request from a ward for a psychologist or OT to initiate an RO programme provides an excellent opportunity for introducing much broader change within the institution. The ward may well be ready for changes of attitude and regime which can and should accompany the implementation of RO.

The RO approach demonstrates the feasibility of changing dementing peoples' behaviour; it readily generalises to less narrowly focussed interventions. Individual programme planning (Holden and Woods, 1982) and modular behavioural programmes (Patterson, 1982) follow on naturally from RO. Far from being potentially damaging, as Hussian (1981) suggests; RO, used adaptively, can be a way forward to better care for elderly people with dementia.

References:

BURTON, M. (1982) Reality orientation for the elderly: A critique. *Journal of Advanced Nursing, 7,* 427-433.

GILLEARD, C. J., MITCHELL, R. G. and RIORDAN, J. (1981) Ward orientation training with psychogeriatric patients. *Journal of Advanced Nursing, 6,* 95-98.

GREENE, J. G., NICOL, R. and JAMIESON, H. (1979) Reality orientation with psychogeriatric patients. *Behaviour Research and Therapy, 17,* 615-617.

GREENE, J. G., TIMBURY, G. C., SMITH, R. and GARDINER, M. (1983) Reality orientation with elderly patients in the community: an empirical evaluation. *Age and Ageing, 12,* 38-43.

GUBRIUM, J. F. and KSANDER, M. (1975) On multiple realities and reality orientation. *Gerontologist, 15,* 142-145.

HANLEY, I. G., McGUIRE, R. J. and BOYD, W. D. (1981) Reality orientation and dementia: a controlled trial of two approaches. *British Journal of Psychiatry, 138,* 10-14.

HANLEY, I. G. (1981) The use of signposts and active training to modify ward disorientation in elderly patients. *Journal of Behaviour Therapy and Experimental Psychiatry, 12,* 241-247.

HOLDEN, U. P. and WOODS, R. T. (1982) *Reality Orientation: Psychological Approaches to the 'Confused' Elderly.* Edinburgh: Churchill Livingstone.

HUSSIAN, R. A. (1981) *Geriatric Psychology: A Behavioural Perspective.* New York: Van Nostrand Reinhold.

PATTERSON, R. L. (1982) (Ed.) *Overcoming Deficits of Aging:* A behavioural approach. New York: Plenum Press.

POWELL-PROCTOR, L., MILLER, E. (1982) Reality orientation: a critical appraisal. *British Journal of Psychiatry, 140,* 457-463.

WOODS, R. T. (1983) Specifity of learning in reality orientation sessions: A single-case study. *Behaviour Research and Therapy, 21,* 173-175

The JBCNS 705 Course and The New RNMS Syllabus

NEIL McNEILL

The Joint Board of Clinical Nursing Studies (J.B.C.N.S.) is a validating and approving body concerning itself with post-basic nurse education. It is important that we clearly differentiate between the two main types of nurse behaviour therapists. A JBCNS 650 is trained, in the main, to deal with acute psychiatric problems, and a JBCNS 700/705 course graduate is trained to deal with a wide range of problems experienced by the mentally handicapped.

The 700 course which has recently been updated to the 705 course is not designed to produce an autonomous clinician, but rather an efficient co-worker in the mental handicap field with behavioural nursing skills. He/she is not being trained to be a 'nurse specialist' in its broadest sense, but the skills they develop will equip them to return to their pre-course position with additional therapeutic and other skills.

The broad aim of the course is to: 'train a nurse to formulate and implement individual and group behavioural programmes involving the family and any other care givers where appropriate in residential settings including the home; and to contribute those skills to the assessment and training of mentally handicapped people within the context of the multidisciplinary team' (Outline Curriculum JBCNS 705).

1. *Who Teaches It?*

For the first 700 course the psychologists who had contributed to the planning of the course did the majority of the teaching and the supervising, with me assisting as best I could (my training previous to this was a six-month behaviour therapy and modification course in Dundee.). Since our first course trained local nurses this established a body of nurses with specialist skills and knowledge who could be used to assist in the teaching and supervision of subsequent courses. Psychologists are by agreement taking more of a backseat role in our new course both in the teaching and the supervision of course members. As the courses further develop, we foresee this backseat role becoming extended with the nurses training and supervising themselves and the psychologists acting as consultants and teachers. Naturally, we do not want to create a narrow behaviourist who knows nothing else than how to manipulate contingencies, so we attempt to establish some depth by drawing on a broad group of non-behaviourists, for example, administrators, to discuss current views, advances in care, philosophies or management.

2. *What are the areas emphasised by the course?*

When looking at the knowledge base required by a nurse, we feel that the area of ethics is often under-discussed. Certainly we see this as a priority, as the buck often stops with the nurse as the programme implementor. Strategies for changing behaviour are obviously covered in detail, as a sound grasp of the theoretical constructs and research evidence is essential. Politics is also an area which demands increasing input because of the expectations placed on a course graduate. I think the need for an understanding of political problems and tactics to minimise these has been reflected closely in many of the contributions to the present book.

As for skills, there are some basic ones which take much of our effort. Objectivity and documentation are obviously essential to the application of good behaviour modification, as is the ability to read, digest and use information contained in for example, a research report. Silly though it may appear, these are extremely difficult skills to teach. One of the reasons for this is that nurses are not, on the whole, academics. They have not had the benefit of an educational upbringing like psychologists who, during their degree courses, have had to come to terms with reading, digesting and assimilating large amounts of information and condensing this into essays. Interviewing and counselling skills are also, for obvious reasons, given a high priority ranking in our course. These are taught, in the main, through role play and guided practice with feed back. Teaching skills are developed gradually throughout the course, with the rationale that one person needs others to help him. This means that the course graduate has to have the confidence to teach and the skill to impart information.

3. *How are student skills assessed?*

Before this can adequately be explained, the course structure and format needs to be revealed. Figure 1 shows the time periods and core subjects covered.

The core skills are broken into behavioural objectives, and the student has to achieve competence in at least 80% of these by the end of each placement. Over the course there are more than 240 objectives to be attempted. In addition to the objectives, students also have to successfully complete a *viva* at the end of each placement and submit and gain a pass for five essays and two extended case studies.

4. *What placements are used for the course?*

Three placements are used for our six students. One is a community support unit in Exeter which offers two separate experiences for students; one with the community team and one with the unit team. The second is in Plymouth, this is a community based service which provides two separate experiences; one in an assessment and training, day and residential unit and the other with the community team. Our third placement is in a unit which was set up to cater for the needs of disturbed men, sited in a large Hospital.

FIGURE 1

3 weeks theory		1 week theory	1 week theory	1 week consolodation
	9 weeks clinical placement	10 weeks clinical placement	10 weeks clinical placement	

Core skills for placement	⎧ Interviewing ⎪ Global ⎪ assessments ⎪ Measuring ⎪ behaviour ⎨ Reinforcers ⎪ Interpretation ⎪ Displaying ⎪ information ⎪ Flexibility ⎩ Liaison skills	Assessment Goal planning Implementation Evaluation Flexibility Liaison skills	Implementation Goal planning Evaluation Generalisation Maintenance Follow-up Teaching M.D.T. functioning

5. *How many referrals might a student deal with?*

Naturally, this may vary depending on the complexity of the problems presented by the clients. On average, a community student will receive and deal with seven or eight clients during an attachment, whilst a student on a community unit attachment might receive and deal with four or five. In the disturbed unit, three or four referrals are the average. The range of course work is broad and we always attempt to ensure students receive a realistic mixture of clients and situations over their nine months.

The New RNMS Syllabus:

It is important to acknowledge that the role of the mental handicap nurse has changed and is changing; the new syllabus reflects this and will hopefully afford us a smooth transition.

The philosophy of the syllabus is outlined in three basic statements:

1. That people with mental handicap have the same rights and as far as possible the same responsibilities as any other member of the community.

2. That people with mental handicap have the right and the need to live like others in the community, and to receive services to meet their changing needs.

3. That people with mental handicap should receive additional help from the professional services to allow the full recognition and expression of their individuality.

81

Nineteen sections are outlined in the syllabus which are as follows:

Core Concepts

1. The Nursing Process
2. Communication
3. Education and the mentally handicapped
4. Sociology of organisations
5. Normalisation and human rights
6. Management
7. Principles of Development
8. Causation and effects of mental handicap
9. Partnership with families

Essential Skills Areas

10. Developing care and training programmes
11. Maintenance of the living environment
12. Children
13. Adolescents
14. Adults
15. The Elderly Person
16. People with multiple handicaps
17. Facilitating integration and rehabilitation
18. Maintaining optimum health
19. Professional development

One of the problems facing implementation of this syllabus is 'Who is going to teach it all?'. Without being disrespecful, there isn't a large number of nurse tutors who could possibly have a lot of practical, or even theoretical knowledge of some of the areas.

Interlaced throughout the syllabus are behavioural techniques, the nursing process, and individual programme planning. Implementing and teaching these approaches can only be done by persons extremely conversant with them. Which leads nicely to another problem 'Where are the students going to get practical experience of these approaches?' Even under the new syllabus learners will still have the majority of their clinical experiences in the wards of hospitals where no such systems operate.

In conclusion, I see the new syllabus as a powerful tool. Used effectively and efficiently, it could make a major impact on the system and its nurses by developing a new 'behavioural' nurse. If people with the knowledge and skills apply these constructively, it is certain that the shape of the mental handicap nurse and the work place would be changed considerably.

References:

GENERAL NURSING COUNCIL (1982) Outline Curriculum JBCNS Course 705. London: General Nursing Council.
GENERAL NURSING COUNCIL (1982) Training Syllabus, Register of Nurses for the Mentally Subnormal. London: General Nursing Council.

Conductive Education

BETTY BUD

Conductive education is a unique form of education originated by Professor Andras Peto, combining physical, cognitive, linguistic and social training in a daily, systematically conducted programme.

Professor Peto, a physician and educationalist, set up the Institute of Conductive Education in Budapest in 1945, in order that motor disabled pre-school children could learn to participate in daily functional activities, e.g. washing, dressing, feeding, walking, in order to be admitted to the state schools at the age of six years.

On discovering conductive education and after visiting the Institute in Budapest, we set up an experimental project based on conductive education for eight severely physically and mentally handicapped children in the Special School in St. Lawrence's Hospital, Caterham. The aim of conductive education is to turn badly functioning children into well-functioning children. Peto said that cerebral palsied children are not sick, therefore need training rather than treatment. The same can be said of mentally handicapped children. In conductive education the whole child is treated as a whole the whole time. In order to do this, Peto introduced a new professional, the Conductor, who combines the role of teacher, physiotherapist, speech therapist, nurse and care assistant in one person, who spends the whole day with the child. By so doing Peto eliminated the segregation, confusion and competition caused by shuttling children between separate experts. The Conductor is the key to the success of the system and works with them in a quiet classroom. Because he/she is with them all the time, he/she knows them intimately, and he/she has the skills to plan an integrated programme based on learning how to overcome their problems. This is quite different from the multidisciplinary team who come together to plan a programme which is implemented by different experts in different places.

Conductive education is a learning method, based on the findings of Pavlov (1928) and his theory that learning processes take place through conditioned reflexes. Peto called the method he used rhythmical intention, using the work of the neuropsychologists Luria (1961) and Vygotsky (1962). By this method the children use overt speech and inner speech to express an intention. This is followed by the movement which is carried out to the rhythms of counting 1 to 5. Vygotsky had a theory that egocentric speech focussed attention on motor function and assisted in difficult motor tasks. Bernstein explained that any voluntary manipulative movement must be a complex functional system, incorporating kinaesthetic and visuo-spatial aspects. Furthermore, that every action consists of a number of elements or chain of consecutive movements. In its initial stages of formation this chain of motor elements is discreet in character. In the formation of a motor skill, this chain of isolated impulses is reduced and the complex movements begin to be formed as a 'kinetic melody'. In conductive education the conductor leads the children into this 'kinetic melody'.

Another important aspect of the system is working in groups, where the children not only see others learning to overcome similar handicaps to themselves, but find the praise and approbation received from their peers and conductors for successful performance greatly motivating for further effort.

In the St. Lawrence's group, proof of the validity of the system was the developing independence, enjoyment, social awareness and understanding of their own problems and determination to overcome them. Of equal importance was the unifying effect the system had on the staff.

References:

LURIA, A. R. (1961) *The Role of Speech in the Regulation of Normal and Abnormal Behaviour.* Oxford: Pergamon.
PAVLOV, I. P. (1927) *The Conditioned Reflex* New York: Dover.
VYGOTSKY, L. S. (1962) *Thought and Language.* Cambridge, Mass.: M. I. T. Press.

Micro-Computers and Severe Mental Handicap

REG MORRIS and JUDITH McBRIEN

Recent developments in microcomputers, coupled with grants towards their purchase has brought computer technology within the budgets of most special education establishments so that there now exists an excellent opportunity to take advantage of this in the education of mentally handicapped children and adults. In a Schools Council report, Green, Hart, McCall and Staples (1982) have discussed the benefits and pitfalls of micro-computers in teaching mentally handicapped children. In concrete terms, some of the benefits of micro-computer methods in the teaching process are: (i) the computer has an ability to generate very rapidly large numbers of examples and non-examples for concept learning; (ii) its capacity for visual simulation may help to bridge the gap between concrete and abstract gradually and consistently. These two aspects can be attained with a great deal less trouble for the teacher than if he/she had to generate this material him/herself. (iii) The computer can provide consistent repetition or practice to aid retention — a procedure that may be wearisome to the human teacher but which is known to be beneficial (e.g. Ellis, 1963). (iv) Individual-ised training can be given by adjusting difficulty levels to suit individual clients. (v) Micros can help with the evaluation of client progress by objective recording and storage of data so that training can begin at the appropriate level and teachers may have access to up-to-date information when considering new educational objectives. The computer can analyse data and produce summaries and graphs far more quickly than can a teacher. (vi) Microcomputers can assist in the operation of devices that would otherwise be beyond the physical capabilities of many mentally handicapped people and thereby increase the range of skills that may be taught.

These and other advantages of microcomputers are realised in two ways — either through Computer Assisted Instruction (C.A.I.) or via Computer Managed Instruction (C.M.I.). In C.A.I. the student learns via direct interaction with the computer or a computer peripheral. Much software is currently available for teaching in *normal* schools but there is little suitable for the severely mentally handicapped pupil. Moreover, there have been few serious attempts to evaluate available software. We have found over forty articles describing software for special education, but an alarming lack of empirical evidence concerning its effectiveness with mentally handicapped populations. Most evaluations of C.A.I. are restricted to anecdotes and informal case reports, and most are with normal school children.

In C.M.I., the computer helps to control the educational programme for each student, but the teacher, rather than the student, interacts directly with the machine. Assessment, selection of individualised teaching programmes and continuous record keeping are examples of such applications. In other words, it is akin to the role of the special educator as conceived today. As statutory demands are made on special educators with regard to special educational needs and individual programme planning, the time saved and the consistency and ease of presentation of information afforded by a microcomputer are going to be of value. Once again, there is a shortage of material suitable for mentally handicapped people.

So far we have discussed only the didactic role of micro-computers. However, they may also assist mentally handicapped people more directly in their interaction with the environment. This function, sometimes referred to as 'information prosthetics', involves the use of micro-electronic technology to compensate for the cognitive deficits of the mentally handicapped in a manner parallel to their use with the physical deficits of the physically disabled. Examples of information prostheses include the use of currently available technology to aid spelling, simple monetary computations and memory. It is also worth noting that micro-electronic methods are used more and more frequently in everyday life. Banking, shopping, telephones and transport are just some examples. Familiarity with these methods is becoming a social 'survival skill' meriting the attention of educators involved in determining curricula for the mentally handicapped.

Reviews in this area are quick to point out the limitations of the new technology. We list here just a few of the more salient ones. (i) There is a notable lack of appropriate software for severely mentally handicapped clients. (ii) Allied to this is the danger, pointed out by Green et al (1982) of fragmenting the curriculum because of the lack of integration in the development of software. (iii) There is a mismatch of skills in that most mental handicap practitioners are computer illiterates, while there is a corresponding ignorance of mental handicap among computer experts. (iv) There is a dearth of empirical evaluation of C.A.I. and C.M.I. with severely mentally handicapped people. (v) There are still limitations in the hardware and software in terms of 'understanding' normal speech and in producing realistic visual material.

Our own work in this area is at a very preliminary stage. We are using an Apple II with an interface which has a number of manipulanda, an automated reinforcer dispenser, stimulus lights, loudspeaker and V.D.U. There is also an ultra-sound motion detector, speech synthesiser and speech analysis facilities. This equipment is situated in a community unit for severely disturbed, severely mentally handicapped young adults. All programmes are being used by nursing staff on a regular basis. Our aim has been to develop software to suit one individual at a time, basing the programme on a knowledge of their developmental level and current training needs. If the same programme is then found to work for other clients then so much the better, but we felt that this was not necessarily going to be the case. Two programmes are noted here. The first was designed for a hyperactive teenager with a developmental level of two to three months. Variable ratio and fixed ratio reinforcement schedules were programmed to reward specified responses and to promote awareness of reinforcement contingencies. Reinforcers can vary from changing patterns on the V.D.U. to sounds, tokens, food or flashing lights. The client is required to make a simple lever press to gain reinforcement on a Fixed Ratio 1 schedule. He receives a ten minute daily session on this programme carried out by his nursing assistant.

The second programme was written for a teenage girl to teach her to count objects. Baselines on her counting skills were used to inform the content of the programme. The number to be counted is spoken by the computer and at the same time is represented on the screen by a corresponding number of lorries. The client responds by pressing a lever the correct number of times. At each press one lorry lights up and the computer says the number aloud. The computer then praises the client using her own name. Again, the client receives a daily session on this programme carried out by her nursing assistant. Results of these programmes will be presented elsewhere, but are mentioned here to illustrate the individuality of programming for a severely mentally handicapped population which we feel is required.

In conclusion, we would like to strike a note of caution with regard to the use of microcomputers with severely mentally handicapped people. While they hold great promise, and while applications of C.M.I. are clear, the case for C.A.I. remains unproven. One needs to be wary of foisting upon severely mentally handicapped people and their carers software which has not been designed specifically for them. There is a need for evaluative research on existing software, contrasting its effects with those of traditional instructional approaches and for careful development of new programmes designed for this population.

References:

GREEN, F., HART, R., McCALL, C. and STAPLES, I. (1982) *Microcomputers in Special Education.* Schools' Council, Programme 4. London: Longman.

Portage as a System of Service Delivery to Pre-School Developmentally Delayed Children

KEVIN HEWITT

Portage is a home-based system of developmental training for young developmentally delayed children. It comprises of specially trained home teachers, working under the supervision of psychologists who have special training and expertise in dealing with developmental problems of infancy and early childhood. The role of the home advisor is to help parents acquire teaching skills appropriate to their developmentally delayed child whilst following a curriculum based on the normal developmental sequence. Precision teaching via 'activity charts' is used by the home advisor to help parents to teach their child. Some home-based training schemes have a management team which monitors the service and advises on policy issues as well as regular meetings between supervisors and home-advisors. Portage is a cost-effective means of servicing families with delayed children, though it is only one of several ways of intervening with this client population.

In at least one comprehensive home visiting scheme, some departure from the original Portage model has been found necessary. Firstly, children admitted to this service are younger and more severely delayed in their development. Many of the children have obvious additional handicaps, and the 'floor' of the Portage checklist has been found to be too advanced. Consequently, checklists have been modified and alternative checklists combining items from both the Behaviour Assessment Battery and original Portage checklists are currently used. Secondly, the effectiveness of activity charts against other commonly used methods of skill training, has recently been systematically tested. Results show that similar levels of skill gain could be obtained with a target setting, as opposed to a detailed activity chart approach. Certain families who respond less well to activity charts can now be offered an alternative type of teaching without necessarily detracting from the effectiveness of the service. Thirdly, closer contact between home advisors, supervisors and paramedical personnel has been encouraged at the clinical level. The presence of paramedical staff at the weekly meetings has prompted better co-ordination of advice to recipient families as well as regularisation of home visits which are often conducted jointly between the home advisor and therapist.

Although guidelines exist for implementation of Portage-type home teaching services, it is apparent that some schemes differ not only in specific details of service provision, but also in a more general way; often in response to local circumstances and financing. It is therefore appropriate to consider which features of the Portage system are essential. The following areas are suggested for investigation:

Supervision of the home advisors and training of the supervisors.
Home Advisors, selection, training and contracts of Home Advisors.
The role of the Management Group.
The role of the Staff Meeting.

As regards the evaluation of the effectiveness of Portage, it is suggested that child-orientated measures which have traditionally been used might yield either overly optimistic or occasionally pessimistic results for certain sub-groups of clients. For instance, an analysis of successfully completed activity charts reveals a highly impressive success rate, but masks the fact that many charts would have been successful even if a child had required physical prompting to achieve the criterion behaviour. Furthermore, the use of standardised developmental tests as outcome measures might provide compelling evidence for service effectiveness for some children, but disappointing results for others.

The Portage approach sets out to teach parents skills relevant to the early education of their developmentally delayed child, and it is therefore suggested that future research might focus upon parental skill acquisition as a more direct evaluation of this type of service. Other directions for research might include comparisons with alternative forms of intervention as well as long-term follow-up of children who have received regular home visiting in the pre-school years and are now in receipt of formal education.

References:

BARNA, S., BIDDER, R. T., GRAY, O. P., CLEMENTS, J. and GARNER, S. (1980) The progress of developmentally delayed pre-school children in a home-training scheme. *Child Care, Health and Development, 6,* 157-164.

BERRY, I. and WOOD, J. (1981) The evaluation of parent intervention with young handicapped children. *Behavioural Psychotherapy, 9,* 358-368.

BIDDER, R. T., HEWITT, K. E. and GRAY, O. P. (1983) Evaluation of teaching methods in a home-based training scheme for developmentally delayed pre-school children. Child Care, Health and Development, 9, 1-12.

BURDEN, R. L. (1979) Intervention programmes with families of handicapped children. *Bulletin of the British Psychological Society, 32,* 137-141.

HOLLAND, F. L. U. and NOAKS, J. C. (1982) Portage in Mid-Glamorgan. *A.E.P. Journal, 5,* 32-35.

KIERNAN, C. and JONES, M. (1977) *Behaviour Assessment Battery.* Windsor: N.F.E.R. Publishing Company.

REVILL, S. and BLUNDEN, R. (1980) *A Manual For Implementing A Portage Home Training Service For Developmentally Handicapped Pre-school Children.* Windsor: N.F.E.R. Publishing Company.

SHEARER, M. S. and SHEARER, D. E. (1972) The Portage project: A model for early childhood education. *Exceptional Children, 36,* 210-217.

Evaluation

Evaluation and Research: An Overview

JOHN HALL

A number of terms, such as monitoring, reviewing, and evaluating, are used in an overlapping way to refer to a range of related procedures. In 'Facing the Challenge', the emphasis throughout has been on different aspects of a range of procedures concerned to improve the lot of chronically handicapped people. While evaluation of staff performance, and evaluation of staff training programmes are of considerable importance, they are thus secondary to the evaluation of client outcome and programme effectiveness. While evaluation of client outcome is relatively well advanced for particular interventions with specific conditions, such as the use of behavioural methods with phobic conditions, less attention has been paid to the evaluation of programmes of service delivery, yet evaluation at this level is needed with the long-term complex therapeutic regimes involved with chronically handicapped people.

In the United States 'program evaluation' has been identified as the most rapidly expanding field of psychology, although there is concern whether this expansion has been conceptually sound. This overview will accordingly look at some aspects of this American work, and consider how useful it might be in a British setting.

Weiss (1975) has suggested that programme evaluation is: 'an enterprise which examines the effects of policies and programs on their targets (individuals, groups, institutions, communities) in terms of the goals they are designed to achieve. By objective and systematic methods, evaluation research assesses the extent to which goals are realised and looks at the factors associated with successful and unsuccessful outcomes. The assumption is that by providing 'the facts', evaluation assists decision makers to make wise choices among future courses of action'.

Programme evaluation is not the same as experimental validation of a technique. Many service innovations cannot be considered as experiments in a scientific sense. Especially with long-term programmes, it is extremely difficult to avoid the impact of such external factors as strikes of direct-care personnel, and changes in government policy with respect to finance of public health care, upon the programme. Some of the design issues in programme evaluation are considered by Jones (1979).

Undoubtedly the growth of evaluative research in the U.S. has been prompted by the requirement of U.S. Federal funding agencies that evaluations of work accompany requests for further Federal money, as shown by the requirement of the Rehabilitation Services Agency. Although Wing and Hailey (1972) published a series of studies looking at psychiatric services in Camberwell, although there has been some evaluation of the 'Worcester project' involving the build-up of psychiatric services to replace Powick Hospital in Worcestershire, and despite the activities of the Health Care Evaluation Project based at Winchester, British funding agencies and British professional workers have not adopted programme evaluation very enthusiastically. Why not?

One reason why evaluation research has developed in America, and a reason why it may develop here, is the change in public attitudes towards the behaviour of public agencies. The changes in British Law towards greater concern for patients' rights and parents' rights (see, for example, the Education Act 1981 and the National Health Act 1983) and demands for greater public accountability, taken with greater financial stringency in public agencies, mean that professional staff will increasingly need to show that they are making the most of what they have. This demonstration may not only require that improvements can be demonstrated in some way, but that potential harm is minimised, and that more effective alternatives to existing models of care have at least been considered. The problem is that direct care staff may well know their patient population well, but tend to be poor at summarizing knowledge about overall outcome of care or about patient characteristics (Posavac and Carey, 1979). Clinical information, in their words 'is too rich for use in understanding the program as a whole', so new methods of data collection, and new ways of thinking about evaluation need to be developed.

One problem facing the potential evaluator is which model of evaluation to choose. Donabedian, in a classic article (1966) drew attention to the different levels of effect which may be evaluated. Structure, or the resources available, may be examined; processes, or the application of those resources, may be examined; or outcome, the end result of the application of the resources, may be examined. The crucial point made by Donabedian is that more resources and better application do not necessarily result in better health care. To take an example, provision of more and better trained nurses on a ward for the elderly does not automatically lead to more interaction between the patients or to a higher level of independent functioning.

One characteristic of the evaluation approach is that some pre-identified goal, or target, of the service is chosen as the outcome criterion. For example, Williamson and his colleagues (1975) defined one goal for health care as 'maximum achievable benefit', so that outcome can then be defined as 'the percentage of maximum acvhievable benefit achieved'. Using this approach, it would be possible to define as the maximum achievable benefit of a programme for people with chronic schizophrenia that 95% of them attended a regular after-care clinic, so that the outcome could then be determined as a percentage of those known people who did attend. For this approach to work, the maximum achievable benefit must be set at a level low enough to be realistic, yet high enough to represent genuine goals to be achieved. The emphasis on goal achievement minimises attention paid to the process whereby the goals are achieved, and glosses over variations in the programme during its execution.

90

Another characteristic is the emphasis on financial factors. Where outcome factors can have a cost attached to them, then potentially a cost-benefit analysis can be carried out, leading to a calculation of the cost per number of functional units of improvement which have occurred. This approach only has value if there is some agreement on the costs which can be attached to subjective indices of improvement. Noble (1977) reviewed 18 cost-benefit analysis studies in the rehabilitation of people with physical handicaps. He found cost-benefit ratios ranging from about 0 (benefit equals cost) to 70 (benefit 70 times the cost). Noble comments that exercises such as this are highly sensitive to the assumptions and operational definitions of the people conducting the exercise.

One approach to the difficulties of the evaluative process is to at least suggest a model that can be used in designing an evaluation programme, even if the model is of less value for *post-hoc* evaluation. A model may at least simply describe the programme: it may also examine the correspondence between the plan of the programme and the reality of its execution; it may look at the possibility of predicting outcome from client characteristics; and some examination of casual effects of one variable on others may be possible. Hawkins and Fremour (1981) have described such a model, as shown in Figure 1.

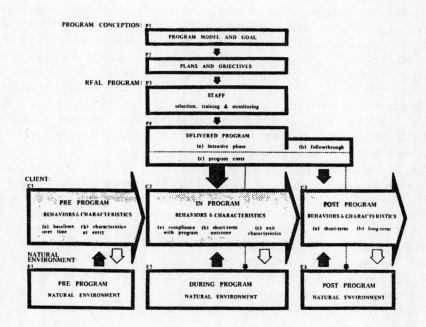

FIGURE 1

91

Going through Figure 1 cell by cell, cell P1 includes, for example, the theoretical model, the relevant legislation, and the original proposal documents for a project. Cell P2 would cover the detailed plans and objectives: a simple descriptive evaluation of the extent to which these were achieved can often be carried out at very low cost. Cell P3 pays attention to the process of staff selection, training and monitoring, addressing such questions as: how much time and money is spent training; what skills do staff have after training? Cell 4 examines the programme as delivered: it would examine the physical environment in which the programme is delivered, and the number and type of follow-up contacts to which patients have been exposed.

Cell C1 essentially answers the question 'Who does the programme serve?' and would supply such information as the age of patients, and their pattern of behaviour before entering the programme. Cell C2 is concerned with in-programme behaviour, and raises the central issue of compliance: a programme can only be effective if clients are actually involved in it and attending its associated activities! Short-term outcomes, such as rate of progress within the programme, would be considered here, as well as characteristics of clients as they leave the programme. Follow-up is covered by cell C3, emphasising that good in-programme results do not necessarily predict good long-term outcome. The natural environment, or setting, of the programme can also be evaluated, such as the behaviour and attitudes of clients' spouses, which might be included in cell E2.

A further major characteristic of the evaluation approach is the attention it pays to the recipients of evaluation reports. Who is interested in the reports, what questions do they want answered, and to what use will any information be put? There is a range of potential audiences, or readerships, for these reports. Some audiences are external to the programme, such as the general public, referral agencies (such as family doctors), and the scientific/professional community who read technical journals. Other audiences are internal to the programme, and in the British health care system would include members of the District Health Authority, Nursing Officers, and of course the patients or clients who have been through the programme. Different audiences will require different sections of the report, presented in different ways, and will require regular monitoring reports at differing frequencies.

All of this American experience should make us cautious about too readily jumping on the evaluation band-waggon. As Adams (1975) has pointed out, models of evaluation may vary along a number of dimensions, such as the subject matter which is analysed, the degree of concern with a programme effectiveness in achieving stated goals, and the amount of emphasis on testing new methods. Parker and Thomas (1980) question a number of assumptions commonly adopted in evaluation research. For example, they quote a study showing a correlation of -.75 between final ability of students on a course, and students ratings of their instructors: in other words, students who learned the most rated their teachers least favourably, which does not encourage faith in at least some types of consumer evaluation. The same paper goes to present other anomalous influences on the evaluation process, under such entertaining titles as 'the Angel's Downfall', and 'the Cherry Tree Syndrome'.

Although the concept of cost is an important one, it can be very difficult to convert non-cash costs linearly into cash equivalents. For example, placing a clinic 20 miles rather than 40 miles from a community might have much less effect on perceived convenience than a reduction from 15 miles away to 5 miles. Similarly, time travelling may be perceived differently to time waiting, so that in some settings waiting at a clinic may be seen as relief from other obligations, and as a socially valued occasion (Sechrest and Cohen, 1980).

The need for relevant outcome measures has already been mentioned. In some fields of physical rehabilitation indices of Activities of Daily Living (ADL) have been used as global outcome measures. These are less relevant for people with a primarily non-medical disability, and accordingly more comprehensive indices incorporating data on social activity are required, such as the Index of Well-Being (IWB) developed by Kaplan, Bush and Berry (1976). In some instances, results are desirable only if they are maintained. Schultz (1976), for example, found that aged people in a residential setting who could control visits by student volunteers were happier and healthier than those people who were visited, but who could not control the visits. However, when the visiting programme stopped, those residents who had been able to control the visits then became worse than the residents who had not been able to control visits.

Despite these reservations, this overview should indicate that the evaluation approach should be considered much more carefully in Britain. The evaluation approach directs our attention to a number of issues which are not covered by traditional research designs. In particular, the approach does not make assumptions about the benefit to the patient which might arise from a staff training programme for example, but requires that that benefit is demonstrable. These issues are particularly relevant to the care and management of people with chronic handicaps, where the facilities for experimentally neat research designs may be limited, and where matters of long-term outcome, and of costs are especially important.

There may be limitations to the approach, but it offers guidance on at least four matters of interest to people contemplating behavioural programmes with severely handicapped people:

1. No patient can benefit from a programme if he is not engaged in it. Compliance is not just about taking pills, but about participation in activities.
2. While cost-benefit analysis may be sensitive to assumptions, at least interventions can be compared making the same assumptions.
3. The idea of pre-identification of goals or targets is a challenge to programme managers to show that their programme is successful not just statistically, but in terms of real benefit to the participants.
4. The requirement to view rehabilitation programmes in this way makes it easier to identify the fit between the information arising from a programme, and the decisions which may purport to be based on that information.

References:

ADAMS, S. (1975) *Evaluation Research in Corrections: A Practical Guide.* Washington: U.S. Department of Justice.
DONABEDIAN, A. (1966) Evaluating the quality of medical care. *Millbank Memorial Fund Quarterly, 44,* 166-206.

HAWKINS, R. P. and FREMOUW, W. J. (1981) A model for use in designing or describing evaluations of mental health or educational intervention programmes. *Behavioural Assessment, 3,* 307-324.

JONES, R. R. (1979) Program evaluation design issues. *Behavioural Assessment, 1,* 51-56.

KAPLAN, R. M., BUSH, J. W. and BERRY, C. C. (1976) Health Status: types of validity for an index of well-being. *Health Services Research, 11,* 478-507.

NOBLE (1977) The limits of cost-benefit analysis as a guide to priority-setting in rehabilitation. *Evaluation Quarterly, 1,* 347-380.

PARKER, R. M., and THOMAS, K. R. (1980) Fads, flaws, fallacies, and foolishness in evaluation of rehabilitation programs. *Journal of Rehabilitation, 46,* 32-34.

POSAVAC, F. J. and CAREY, R. G. (1979) A method of program evaluation in rehabilitation settings. *Journal of the Association of Rehabilitation Nurses, 4,* 5-7.

SCHULTZ, R. (1976) Effects of control and predictability on the physical and psychological well-being of the institutionalized aged. *Journal of Personality and Social Psychology, 33,* 563-573.

SECHREST, L. and COHEN, R. Y. (1980) Evaluating outcomes in health care. In G. C. Stone, F. Cohen and N. E. Adler. (Eds.). *Health Psychology — A Handbook.* San Francisco: Jossey Bass.

WEISS, C. H. (1975) Evaluation research in political context. In E. L. Struening and M. Guttentag (Eds.). *Handbook of Evaluation Research.* Beverley Hills: Sage.

WILLIAMSON, J. W., ARONVITCH, S., SIMONSON, L., RAMIREZ, C. and KELLY, D. (1975) Health accounting: An outcome-based system of quality assurance: Illustrative application to hypertension. *Bulletin of New York Academy of Medicine, 51,* 727-738.

WING, J. K. and HAILEY, A. M. (1972) (Eds.) *Evaluating a Community Psychiatric Service.* London: Oxford University Press.